Statistics without Math

WILLIAM E. MAGNUSSON,
Instituto Nacional de Pesquisas da Amazônia,
Brazil

GUILHERME MOURÃO,
Empresa Brasileira de Pesquisas Agropecuárias Pantanal,
Brazil

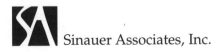 Sinauer Associates, Inc.

editora
PLANTA

North American Distributor:
Sinauer Associates, Inc.
23 Plumtree Road
Sunderland, MA. 01375 U.S.A.

Fax: 413-549-1118
Internet: www.sinauer.com

Brazilian Distributor:
Editora Planta
Rua José M.S. Paranhos, 123 Sala 26
86061-270
Londrina PR

Telephone: (43) 3357-1108 / 9102-4620
Internet: www.editoraplanta.com.br

Brazilian Cataloging-in-Publication Data
A catalog record for this title is available from the Brazilian Library
ISBN 85-902002-2-1

Published by Editora Planta
Rua José M.S. Paranhos, 123 Sala 26
86061-270
Londrina PR
In association with
Sinauer Associates, Inc.

Printed in Brazil 2004
6 5 4 3 2 1

Dedication

To Graeme Caughley whose philosophy pervades this book,
but who unfortunately did not live to enrich it
with his indomitable writing style.

Acknowledgements

Many people contributed to the development of this book; principally our students. However, we can mention only some of those that contributed to the final form. The major structure of the book was developed while William E. Magnusson was a research fellow at Griffith University, Australia, supported by a post-doctoral scholarship from CAPES. Carla Catterall and Marc Hero made that fellowship possible and productive. Mike Dale reviewed the English version of the book and corrected the many grammatical, statistical, and philosophical oversights. The Portuguese version benefited from the careful revisions done by Helena Bergallo, Isis Medri, Agostinho Catell, and a multitude of students in our courses. Had it not been for the support of our editor, Efraim Rodrigues and the staff at Editora Planta, the Portuguese version of the book would have taken much longer to see the light of day. Likewise, the English version may never have materialized if it were not for the support and encouragement of Stuart Pimm, and Andy Sinauer and the staff at Sinauer Associates, Inc.

About the Authors

William "Bill" Magnusson has been a researcher at INPA (Instituto Nacional de Pesquisas da Amazônia) since 1979. His research interests involve the ecology of Amazonian organisms, the design of integrated research programs, and effective scientific communication.

Guilherme "Gui" Mourão has been a researcher at Embrapa Pantanal since 1987. His research interests involve the ecology and management of large vertebrates.

Table of Contents

## CHAPTER 1

*"The last thing the world needs is
another statistics book."*

Introduction

The last thing the world needs is another statistics book. There are already a great
many that competent statisticians can refer to, and many of these are written with
wit and style. Why then would two ecologists, who are quite incompetent mathematicians, write a book that deals with statistical concepts? One reason is that we
have been teaching a basic statistics course for years that our students claim has
revolutionized their ability to understand statistics. The other is that we realize
that our course is largely remedial. Nothing we teach is truly revolutionary and
we spend an inordinate amount of time on basic concepts that the student
unlearned during standard statistical courses. In fact, both students and teachers
have asked us for a basic text to accompany the course.

Tukey (1980) noted that, "Students who have never been exposed to confirmatory seem to learn exploratory more quickly." The major errors in sampling design
result from disregard of the basic logical concepts that most students worry about
before their attention is diverted by the mathematics of statistics. Platt (1964) put
it very eloquently in the following passage:

> **"You can catch phenomena in a logical box or in a mathematical box. The logical
> box is coarse but strong. The mathematical box is fine grained but flimsy. The
> mathematical box is a beautiful way of wrapping up a problem, but it will not hold
> the phenomena unless they have been caught in a logical box to begin with."**

Guttman (1985) described the difference as being similar to the difference between
scaffolding and substance. Hopefully we can teach some substance along with the
scaffolding.

There are, of course, statistical mathematics that can help us see the world more clearly. However, these are not the concepts emphasized in standard statistics courses. Students often ask us why standard statistical texts do not deal with these subjects. The answer is that they do. If you took the first few pages of each chapter of any major textbook and strung them together, they would tell a story very similar to ours. Other authors have realized the need for a short overview that puts all of the analyses into a logical framework. At the end of the first chapter of his book, Harris (1975) wrote, "Why read the rest of this book? It must be conceded that a full understanding of the heuristic descriptions of the preceding section would put the student at about the 90th percentile of, say, doctoral candidates in psychology in terms of ability to interpret multivariate statistics."

Few people read Harris' first chapter or the first chapters of any statistics text. The researcher is interested in the interactions of several factors and somebody says, "You need multiple regression (or principal components analysis, or factorial analysis of variance, or some other apparently complicated procedure), so go to page 365." The author of the textbook went to great pains to present a logical sequence that gradually builds the understanding necessary to use the information presented on page 365. However, almost no one will read the book cover to cover. We have never read any conventional statistics book cover to cover in the order that the author envisioned. However we want you to read this book in full, so we kept it very short.

This book is about the basic statistics and experimental design that a student needs in order to understand ecological literature. By basic, we do not mean picking colored balls from a barrel or using analysis of variance to compare growth rates of sorghum in fields with three different levels of fertilizer. Those questions are not basic; they are trivial. Admittedly, the course we give takes three days (24 hours of lessons) to get the student to simple comparisons, but that is not the endpoint. If, after 10 days, the student does not understand the basics of multiple regression, factorial analysis of variance, multivariate statistics, and path analysis, they will not be able to read the literature.

Literacy is the starting point for academic learning.

There are many levels at which any subject can be approached. We have targeted the intermediate level that is given short shrift in most books and courses. However, we believe that it is the most important. The choice of a level at which to start is a highly personal and critically important decision. We illustrate this with an emotive analogy. To learn about firearms, you could begin by taking courses on ballistics and materials science. Alternatively, you could read the gun manufacturer's brochures whose perspective and opinions undoubtedly favor the firearms industry, and focus on how the possession of a firearm can secure and protect you from a potential threat, rather than the dangers and threat of the firearm itself.

We would start by teaching that guns are designed to kill things and there are practical and ethical considerations in relation to their use. We do not claim that the levels we focus on are all-encompassing. They are just the most important to us.

We believe that mathematical treatises on statistics are as important as materials science or subcellular physiology, but maybe that is not the best place to begin to gain practical understanding of statistics. Likewise, we recognize that statistics, like a gun, is a tool to promote cultural identity.

> **However, we believe that the use of statistics as a practical tool and a means of communication is a better place to start.**

You may not need to read this book. If you answer yes to all of the questions in Table 1.1, you have all the major concepts necessary for planning studies and you can immerse yourself in the fine-grained mathematical box. Unfortunately, most people who answer yes to all of the questions in Table 1.1 simply lack the training to understand how many simple things can go wrong.

More dangerous still are those researchers who believe that mathematics can cure a lack of understanding the concepts alluded to in Table 1.1. If you do not have those concepts right, no amount of calculating formulas by hand, plugging data into computers, or mathematical theorems can make your work useful. This book will not make you competent in all the areas mentioned in the table. In fact we could write a book about each one. We fully agree with Harris (1975), who said, "I have not met anyone who could develop an understanding of any area of statistics without performing many analyses of actual sets of data—preferably data that were truly important to him." We can, however, introduce you to the concepts.

A major problem with statistics books is that they are written by statisticians. Researchers often have problems with traditional statistics books because the researcher may lack the statistician's ability to see the world in abstract mathematical terms. Our book starts with real-world observations and shows how statistics can be used to answer questions about them. Statisticians have realized for a long time that statistical understanding can only come from a basic grounding in data collection and inspection of the raw data (e.g., Deming 1975, Tukey 1980).

Our course basically follows the recommendations of the American Statistical Association/Mathematical Association of America joint curriculum committee (see Figure 1 in Moore 1997). The major difference is that we teach the concepts using simple graphs and, where necessary, analogy. Whereas a standard statistics course spends one day explaining the concepts and nine days dealing with the mathematics, our course spends 10 days exploring the concepts in relation to the

Table 1.1 A Guide to Planning your Study

Are you ready to start collecting data?
If you reply "yes" to all of these questions you do not need to read this book.

1. Have you decided what the target of your study is (dependent variable)?

2. Can your dependent variable be measured objectively, and have you asked other researchers whether they consider your measure objective?

3. Have you consulted with all of the other members of your research team to make sure they have the same aims?

4. Have you drawn a flow chart that shows which variables influence the dependent variable and the relationships among the independent variables?

5. Are all members of your team collecting data on the same scale and from the same places so that the results can be integrated at the end?

6. Have you decided what your universe of interest is and do all of the team members agree on this?

7. Have you drawn a map or a conceptual diagram that shows your samples in relation to the universe of interest?

8. Have you drawn hypothetical scatterplots that show the number of independent observations, the expected variability in the data, and the expected magnitude of effects?

9. Have you optimized the size, shape, orientation, and distribution of your sampling units so that variability in the dependent variable is due mainly to the independent variables you are investigating?

10. Is the scale of your sampling appropriate to the scale of your question(s)?

11. Have you decided whether you are interested mainly in direct effects, indirect effects, or overall effects?

12. Have you decided whether your results will be used mainly for estimating whether an effect exists, estimating the magnitude of an effect under present conditions, or predicting what will happen if conditions change?

13. Do you feel confident that your statistics training has prepared you to undertake the operations described above?

14. Based on those operations, do you feel confident that your statistics training has prepared you to choose the appropriate analysis before going into the field?

15. If you answered "yes" to question 13, have you consulted with a statistician and shown them the results of all the operations listed above to make sure you are not fooling yourself?

16. Will using these statistics help you communicate with your target audience?

most commonly used techniques and leaves the mathematics to subsequent courses or private study. This approach works well for students who have never had a statistics course, and for students and professional researchers who have previously completed advanced courses in statistics. Some of our most enthusiastic students have been lecturers who teach university-level statistics courses.

Most of our students express a wish to deepen their mathematical understanding in order to build on the logical concepts we discuss, and most say that they would like to repeat their previous statistics courses. This is a surprising response, since most mathematical-based statistics courses aggravate the math phobia felt by most biologists. There are many forms of intelligence, and mathematical proficiency is only one of them (Goleman 1995).

We put a lot of emphasis on communication. One of the problems with statistical techniques is that each discipline has its own characteristic sampling scales and statistical analyses. Increasing pressure is being put on financing agencies to support "applied" projects, and those agencies are pressuring researchers to submit integrated projects. These are usually called multidisciplinary or interdisciplinary studies. The principal author of the project therefore has to collate the contributions of the individual researchers to present a coherent proposal. As the principal author does not have experience in each field of study, he or she typically accepts the sampling designs presented by their colleagues. This leads to a team working in the same place, often shoulder to shoulder, and hopefully communicating with each other. This is undoubtedly a good thing, but it does not necessarily lead to an integrated analysis of the data.

Even before analysis takes place, problems may arise with the management of the database. Sometimes, creation of the database, rather than interpretation of the data, becomes the aim of the exercise (Hale 1999). Very often the results are unintelligible to the intended audience (Brown 1997).

> **Most of the studies are published independently in specialized journals, and the integrated results expected by the financing agency do not happen.**

Most scientists are conservative, socially-sensitive people who do not like to be seen as different by their peers. In this case, "peers" means others in their discipline and not others in the "integrated" team. They may regard statistics as a cultural badge rather than as a means of communicating objective information (Guttman 1985). Salsburg (1985) goes so far as to refer to statistics as a religion. The team leader therefore faces the difficult task of convincing team members to adjust their sampling regimes to that of the global question and not to the standards of their discipline. They may have little idea of how to integrate the various sampling protocols, and even less understanding of the mathematical consequences of not doing so.

A simple solution would be for the team leader to undertake advanced courses in mathematics and statistics, simultaneously maintain their political contacts, and delay the research until they feel mathematically competent. It is like asking

Figure 1.1

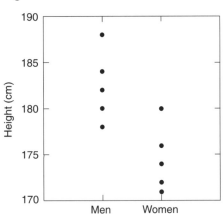

a miner to become a fisherman; great in theory but not so appealing when the person starves or drowns. This book is designed to give a mathematically naïve team leader and the members of the team the background necessary to understand the need for, and limitations on, an effective sampling protocol, without becoming a professional mathematician. All of the concepts in this book are presented with a minimum of mathematics; we provide only what is necessary for the researcher to communicate with a statistician when he or she decides that specialized advice is necessary, and to understand some of the jargon that other team members may be in the habit of using.

We assume that readers can interpret a simple graph such as Figure 1.1, which describes some measurements of height for a group of men and women. We try to show that the most useful statistical tests produce results that can be interpreted in terms of simple graphs such as this. Sampling design and statistical manipulations are rarely useful if they produce results that are more complex than Figure 1.1. It is our belief that the concepts behind most statistical analyses, and the results they produce, can be taught graphically and we wrote this book to try to convince you of that.

What Is Sampling Design?

Sampling design is figuring out how to collect the data so that you will have the best chance of making a good decision.

Most of sampling design is common sense, though we will show in later chapters some examples of how some simple models can help reveal hidden patterns. Here we give an example that shows how a small difference in the sampling scheme can totally change answerable questions.

Our story concerns a species of marmoset that occurs in only one reserve and is thought to be declining. There is anecdotal evidence that this small monkey species occurs in higher densities in parts of the reserve with higher densities of trees, and this has implications for the acquisition of land on the borders of the reserve in order to increase total reserve size. The Wildlife Authority commissions a two-year study to determine whether the species is indeed declining and also whether its density is associated with tree density. Biologist A is contracted and

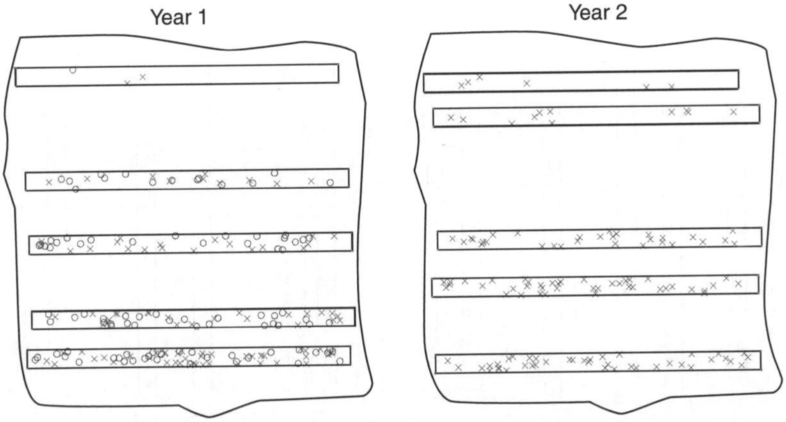

Figure 1.2

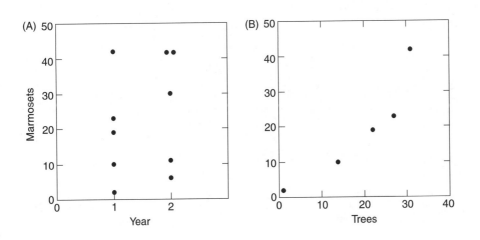

decides to use long, thin plots to count marmosets and trees in one year, and another set of plots to compare marmoset densities between years. The resulting maps are shown in Figure 1.2, in which the circles represent trees, and the crosses represent individual marmosets.

Biologist A's results are presented in the graphs shown in Figure 1.3. Figure 1.3A does not show any convincing difference in marmoset densities between year 1 and year 2. However, there is a strong tendency for marmoset densities to be higher where plant densities are higher (Figure 1.3B).

A conservation organization is suspicious of the government's intentions and contracts Biologist B to carry out a parallel study. Biologist B uses an almost identical design, except that Biologist B places the plots at 90° to those of Biologist A (Figure 1.4).

Figure 1.3

Figure 1.4

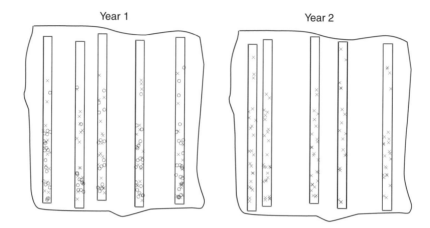

Year 1   Year 2

Biologist B's results, (shown in Figure 1.5), indicate a convincing difference in marmoset densities between years (Figure 1.5A), but there is little relationship between tree density and marmoset density (Figure 1.5B).

The two biologists came to completely opposing conclusions. However, the only difference in experimental design is the direction of the transects. In fact, the two biologists studied the same data. Figure 1.6 shows one plot used by each biologist in the same diagram.

None of the results were incorrect. Biologist A's design detected a relationship between plants and marmosets. A different sampling scheme using square or circular quadrats might have been equally effective. The design used by Biologist B was superior for detecting differences among years, and square plots, circular plots, or any less elongated sampling unit, would have been inappropriate for this question.

Figure 1.5

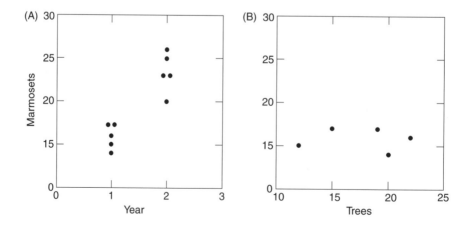

Year 1 Year 2 **Figure 1.6**

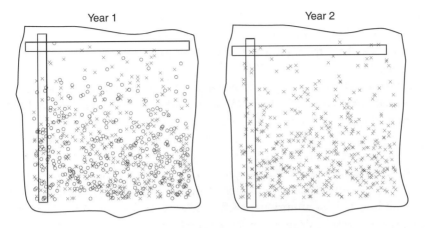

In a situation like this one, in which there is a strong gradient in densities across the area to be surveyed, the orientation, shape, and size of the sampling units determines the questions that can be answered. Caughley and Sinclair (1994; see Chapter 12) give examples for vertebrates, Stern (1998) gives an example for plants, and Johnson et al. (1999) discuss sampling habitat features. Krebs (1998) discusses general aspects of sampling unit shape and size.

Even though there may be no strong gradient, organisms are always clumped at some scale. We cannot give a detailed explanation of selecting sampling units in this book. However, unless the shape and size of the sampling unit is appropriate for the question, none of the more complicated techniques we will discuss in future chapters will be of any use for seeing patterns more clearly, or for communicating what we see. Tukey (1980) emphasized that:

"Finding the right question is often more important than finding the right answer."

We cannot help you very much with this as it involves insight, experience, and curiosity. However, reading Tukey (1980) and Guttman (1985) might help you to get on the right track. It is not enough that the questions are interesting; you have to be able to respond to them in a manner such that they give rise to hypotheses that can be refuted (see Chapter 5). Questions such as, "Is there life after death?" are obviously very interesting, but defy attempts to derive hypotheses that we can test.

Sampling design is about understanding the concepts that are important at each step in the process, from the planning, to the execution, analysis, and publication. This book is not a substitute for a conventional statistics text. It contains no information that cannot be found in any reasonably complete statistical textbook for biologists if you know where to look. It is also not a "how-to-use" book for computer programs (see Dytham [1999] for an introduction to statistical computing). It is not a "how" book. It is a "why" book, and covers only the major principles that researchers must understand in order to use conventional statistics in an intelligent way.

We have not tried to be comprehensive. In fact, we believe that this book is most useful for what it leaves out. We agonized over the important and interesting details that had to be omitted. Our experience with students and researchers is that too much information retards understanding of the concepts, but armed with the concepts, the researcher can soon discover the details. We have not covered topics that most researchers seem to understand. The subject matter was chosen to cover those areas that students and researchers do not get an adequate understanding of in standard statistics courses, and that cause the most frequent breakdown in communication among researchers.

We have given a minimum of references since most of what we cover can be found in any major statistics textbook. Most readers will find that brief summaries are adequate for an initial understanding of the material cited. However, teachers are advised to refer to the original literature rather than to our necessarily brief summaries of it. Teachers will also benefit from reading *The Lady Tasting Tea: How Statistics Revolutionized Science in the Twentieth Century* by Salsburg (2001), a discussion of the personalities behind modern statistics, and *The History of Statistics: The Measurement of Uncertainty before 1900* by Stigler (1986), which gives the ontogeny of statistical concepts beginning in the early 1700s. The references we give are strongly biased towards conceptual and philosophical approaches, rather than mathematical techniques. We have been a little more liberal with technical references in the section on multivariate statistics, because it is difficult to do even an overview of this complex topic.

What We Hope You Get from This Book

There are important concepts that underlie most scientific communication. In order to communicate these concepts we have to use examples, and occasionally we need to do some sums. Therefore, even though we have tried to keep the story as simple as possible, we undoubtedly will distract you with details in some places. It is very important that you read this section to get an overview of important concepts. The order of chapters is slightly different from the order of presentation in our course because the teacher has a much greater role in sewing things together in the classroom. Teachers may prefer to skip first to Chapter 14, *Tips for Teachers*, which can be found online at **www.sinauer.com/swm**, and also at **www.editoraplanta.com**.

Outline of the book

- Chapter 2 *Flow Charts and Scientific Questions.* Throughout the book we refer to flow charts that describe our ecological hypotheses. No statistical test can be interpreted except in relation to a flow chart, though you will probably not understand this until the end of Chapter 10. At this stage, the flow chart is important because it forces you to be explicit about your goals and to understand the difference between variables that cause effects (independent variables) and variables that are affected (dependent variables). This chapter also includes a very short discussion of the importance of scale in ecology. Scale is related to problems noted in Chapter 2, and also in Chapter 10.

- Chapter 3 *Describing Things: Some "Scientific" Conventions and Some Useful Techniques.* This is as close as we come to a standard statistics course. However, the formulas do not matter. It is important for you to realize that concepts such as "standard deviation" can be visualized on graphs, and that some others, such as "variance" are not easy to visualize. We exploit standard errors to teach some concepts in the course (see *Tips for Teachers*). However, it is not necessary to memorize formulas, and techniques involving concepts that are not easy to visualize will be explained by analogy in subsequent chapters. Most importantly, this chapter introduces the concept of "deviation" and allows you to interpret the literature. We hope to convince you that most of the "descriptive" statistics hide rather than reveal data, and we introduce (or reintroduce) you to the most important tool in scientific communication, the dispersion graph (scatterplot).

- Chapter 4 *How Much Evidence Is Enough?* This chapter introduces you to the relationship between strength of inference and the number of points on a dispersion graph. It also discusses information that doesn't increase the strength of our inferences, which has become known among ecologists as pseudoreplication. You should learn to recognize, or at least suspect, spatial, temporal, phylogenetic, and technical pseudoreplication. You should understand that no observation is inherently valid or inherently a pseudoreplicate. This depends entirely on the question.

- Chapter 5 *When Highly Improbable Means Very Unlikely.* In this chapter, we introduce you to Popperian philosophy, which underpins most mainstream statistical analyses. It is not possible to understand the structure of most statistical tests unless you understand the concepts behind Popperian philosophy. It is the basis of "decision trees" and other scientific procedures that do not necessarily involve any mathematics. Science without philosophy is dangerous, and so are statistics.

- Chapter 6 *How to Avoid Accumulating Risk in Simple Comparisons.* In this chapter we introduce analysis of variance (ANOVA) of categorical factors. We give the first explicit discussion of Type II errors, even though they are often more important than the errors focused on by most statistical techniques. Our discussion of Type II errors is very brief, so if you do not have a good understanding of their implications, you should read some of the texts we cite. Although the simple ANOVA is presented as a way of avoiding the accumulation of risk, the most important concept to be learned in this chapter is the unique partitioning of variability among factors and the residual. If you cannot understand this in our simple graphs, you will not be able to understand any of the most commonly used statistical techniques.

- Chapter 7 *Analyses for a World with All Shades of Gray.* ANOVA of continuous factors, which is generally called "regression," is discussed in this chapter. From reading this chapter you should learn that the world consists of continuous variables and that making continuous variables categorical is often unproductive and misleading. However, you should also understand that the concept of partitioning sources of variation applies to continuous variables as much as it does to categorical variables. In fact, ANOVA of categorical factors (referred to as analysis of variance in most textbooks), is just a special case of regression. There are other ways of attacking these simple problems that we defer to Chapter 11 so as not to break the logical sequence. (This is not necessary in the classroom situation; see *Tips for Teachers.*)

- Chapter 8 *Real-World Problems: More Than One Factor.* This title is a bit pretentious on our part. In fact it is not very "real-world," it just shows that more complex models are necessary in order to begin answering ecological questions. Unfortunately, too many researchers believe that these analyses model real-world situations. The analyses are still based on simple linear additive models that allow unique partitioning of the effects of the factors. Do not proceed to the next chapter unless you understand the concept of unique allocation of variance among several factors and the concept of interactions among factors.

- Chapter 9 *Which Variables Should I Analyze Statistically?* We probably do not answer this question in this chapter. The insight and experience necessary for optimum variable selection are part of the naturalist's art and cannot be taught from a book. However, we use the concepts discussed in previous chapters and examples to show you what to avoid when selecting variables.

- Chapter 10 *More Complex Models: Stringing Things Together.* We continue to utilize linear additive models to model the world in this chapter. However, here we show that, except in very simple and often trivial situations, unique variability that can be attributed to each factor generally does not exist. This chapter should bring you full circle to see the importance of the flow charts that were described in Chapter 2. You must understand the differences among direct, indirect, and overall effects of factors, and why none of the statistical tests can be interpreted except in relation to a flow chart.

- Chapter 11 *Straightening the World: Transformations and Other Tricks.* Logically, this should be part of Chapter 7, and that is how we present it in the classroom. However, in a book, it distracts from the logical discussion of the variance allocation techniques which form the basis of over 90% of the statistics found in ecological literature. The techniques described in this chapter use a variety of methods to estimate the parameters that mathematically describe our models, and they can often deal with complex curves. However, they are used infrequently because they generally do not allocate unique variance, and cannot be used to determine the relative importance of factors unless we do some complex computer simulations, or we are willing to divide factors into "significant" and "nonsignificant" categories. After appreciating the limitations of the variance–allocation techniques, advanced researchers may consider using more of these techniques to refine their models.

- Chapter 12 *Multivariate Statistics: Cutting Down the Trees to Better See the Forest.* Fools rush in where wise men fear to tread. Unfortunately, the inexperienced also rush into multivariate statistics. Many students (and professors) think that multivariate statistics are a panacea. Very often, students can generate huge matrices of data that impress, even though there is insufficient replication to analyze even one factor. However, if students understand the relationships between the patterns that can be seen on graphs or tables, and the patterns that the multivariate techniques search for, there is some chance that the results will not just be statistical artifacts. Even if students will not be using multivariate techniques, they need to know the general principles so that they can read the literature. We have tried to show those general principles without resorting to mathematics, and also to highlight some of the most common pitfalls of them. You should at least be able to conceptualize the relationship between phantom dimensions and real gradients before leaving this chapter.

- Chapter 13 *How to Write Better Backwards.* One of the hardest parts of research is presenting conclusions in a logical fashion so that readers can see the relationship between the question, the graphs, and the conclusions. The last printed chapter gives tips on how to do this.

- Chapter 14 *Tips for Teachers* Not included in this text, Chapter 14 can be found on the web at **www.sinauer.com/swm.** This chapter is intended for teachers and explains the teaching methods we have found work best in lectures, and give examples that can be used in class exercises.

## CHAPTER 2

"Science is an art,
and art is about communication."

Flow Charts and Scientific Questions

Science is an art, and art is about communication. A painter sees a landscape, determines what the essence of the landscape is (e.g., warmth, gaiety, loneliness, majesty), and represents that essential quality two-dimensionally using color, texture and form. The artist's objective is to stimulate the same feelings in the person viewing the painting as the painter felt when originally looking at the landscape. Depending on the school of art the painter belongs to, they may wish to say something about the landscape or something personal, or both.

A scientist does much the same thing. An ecologist looking at a landscape may believe that it can be reduced to an essential quality (e.g., competition, mutualism, physical restraints, or metabolism) and they represent that essential quality two-dimensionally using words, graphs, and mathematical formulas. Of course, the scientist would like to believe that their representation is objective, and the only one a rational person could make. However, from personal experience and study of the history of science, the scientist knows that their representation is only partial and may be misleading. Therefore, alternatives are considered and the probability of being incorrect is calculated. This process is formalized in the mathematics of inferential statistics. Hopefully, the scientist will say a maximum about the landscape and a minimum about their personal opinion.

The most important thing a research team leader can do is to produce a two-dimensional diagram of the system that is being investigated. We call such a diagram a flow chart. However, an engineer calls the process systems analysis, a psychologist calls it causal modeling, and a statistician calls it structural equation modeling. Ecologists often do path analyses. The details of methods do not matter at this stage. What is important to understand is that everyone facing complex problems turns to similar techniques, and these techniques are not the property of any one discipline.

There is an art to making flow charts and there are a few basic rules. Only practice confers competence. We find that flow charts are easier than the more complex models for students to understand, and therefore are a good place to start. Teachers and more advanced students should look at the book edited by Higashi and Burns (1991) for an introduction to some other ways of linking the elements of ecosystems.

Start by deciding on what you will be studying. This must be something measurable. "Environmental quality," "conservation status," and "social justice" have no dimensions, or at least have no dimensions that are recognized by all readers. What is it that you want to measure? Environmental quality can refer to conditions that give humans long life expectancies or conditions that allow humans to practice a wide range of outdoor activities. Alternatively, it can refer to conditions that allow the perpetuation of the plant and animal communities that existed when human populations were much smaller, or any one of a multitude of conditions that people consider to be indicators of "quality."

It is best to involve the whole team in the process of deciding what the goals of the study are, despite the fact that goals are also often stated by the financing agency. This part of the process is usually the most difficult, and for this reason it is the one skipped over in most proposals.

There are no implied or tacit goals in a research proposal.

Either the goal is stated explicitly or the team leader is confused, incompetent, or dishonest. Harsh words, but vague goals waste time and money, and jeopardize the credibility of the scientists. Hobbs (1988) gives a very funny, but perhaps tragic, flow chart that models the contributions of ecological research to decision-making.

Every wasted research dollar could have otherwise been used to save the lives of underprivileged children. We have worked in places of extreme poverty and must admit to being intolerant of wasted research efforts. Many texts on decision-making are available and we will not discuss this topic any further here. Introductory discussions can be found in Tukey (1960, 1980) and Chapter 1 of Caughley and Sinclair (1994). A more statistical discussion of the problems of selecting goals and measures for integrating studies can be found in Osenberg et al. (1999). We assume that a goal or variable to be investigated has been defined and proceed next to the problem of deciding what factors might affect that variable and how.

Constructing an Initial Model

You can start with the premise that everything is connected to everything else and try to put everything into your model. This is analogous to the painter trying to put an entire mountain on his canvas—a waste of time. Conversely, you can make a system so simple that it bears no resemblance to the real world, which is more wasted effort. Your model must be simple enough to be manageable, but complex enough to capture the essence of the problem. This is the art of the scientist.

A good discussion of model building can be found in Starfield and Bleloch (1991). Readers who are comfortable with very complicated mathematics should consult Burnham and Anderson (1998). However, we are interested in a much more general level than are those authors.

Model-building is an art that comes with experience.

Do not be ashamed if your first models do not communicate much. Even a bad model shows the limitations of the researcher, or the data, and these are useful things to know.

In this chapter, and throughout the book, we are going to deal with models and their assumptions. Model building sometimes appears to be a technical process. However, models involve philosophical concepts that are more complex than the mathematics. We present two quotes from Allen (1998) that reflect our philosophical viewpoint:

No model that is other than a replica of the material system itself can be a complete representation of the material system for all situations. Therefore, all models are wrong in the sense of being different from the observation. Clearly that sense of right and wrong has no power, so rightness and wrongness of a model that is logically consistent are beside the point.

All assumptions are false at some level, so correctness of assumptions is again beside the point. Science is not about finding the answers to everything; it is about finding the situations in which one can get away with an assumption—and still have the model give the desired behavior.

If you want absolute, all-encompassing answers, we suggest that you abandon this book now and seek theological answers to your questions.

We start with a simple example that relates to an ecological question (Figure 2.1). However, the same logic can be applied to studies at other scales, such as physiological investigations in the laboratory or questions about biogeographical patterns at continental scales.

The flow chart in Figure 2.1 is an obvious simplification and not one amenable to analysis in its present form. However, we will use it to discuss the mechanics of constructing one. This preliminary flow chart is important because it illustrates our initial hypotheses and assumptions. The researcher is obviously interested in the density of crayfish, presumably because the species is of economic importance or is considered to be in danger of extinction, or for some other reason that justifies spending research funds. If you find that the team members cannot agree on the overall goal, you should re-think the problem before submitting a proposal.

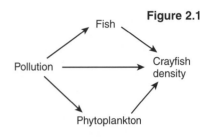

Figure 2.1

We also infer from the flow chart in Figure 2.1 that the team believes that the most important factors affecting the density of the crayfish are fish, phytoplankton, and pollution.

> Hopefully, the researchers use experience, information from the literature, and common sense to decide what factors are worth studying.

Many other factors that could be potentially important, such as bird predation, substrate type, and disease organisms are not included. This is a subjective decision, and the researchers may be wrong. However, they have courageously shown what they believe to be priorities for investigation and the reader can easily see what has been left out. The researchers might be criticized by armchair biologists who can see many other things that could have some trivial effect. This is the price of honesty and integrity, but some of the reviewers may actually offer constructive criticisms.

Flow charts are fundamental to most models used in science, but depending on what flows along the arrows, the questions and the statistical techniques change. In this initial diagram, the arrows merely indicate the direction of influence and they indicate flow in only one direction. A two-headed arrow would indicate that both variables influence each other. If there were no heads on the arrow, it would indicate that the variables change in unison, but that neither directly affects the other. Although theoretically possible, neither of the latter two situations is useful for modeling and you should look for a variable that might explain the relationship.

Figure 2.2

Figure 2.2 shows a correlation that might be replaced by Figure 2.3. If two variables appear to have a causal relationships as shown in Figure 2.4, we might be able to include other factors, such as those shown in Figure 2.5.

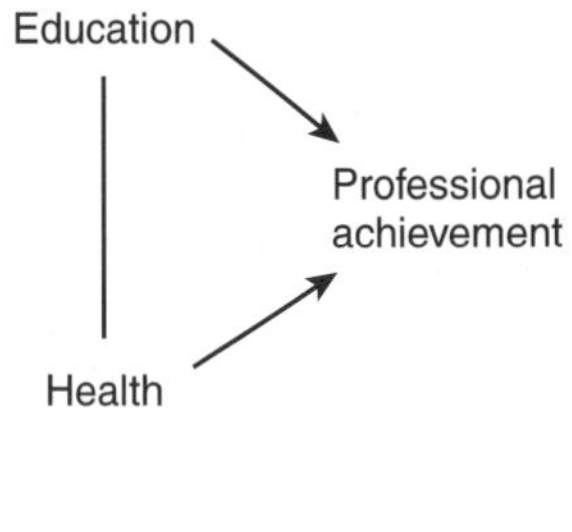

Figure 2.3

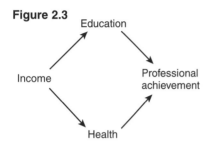

This exercise results in diagrams that show the factors that we believe are important, and what their relationships are. All of the models presented thus far could do with a lot of work, and it may be difficult to see them as vital starting points for scientific studies. They are not unnecessarily complex, and they do not contain any of the hieroglyphics we usually associate with scientific papers, such as "$P < 1$" or "$\chi^2 = \ldots$" Surprisingly however, such diagrams are necessary for interpreting most statistical analyses. Scientific studies investigate one, or sometimes several, of the pathways in a flow chart. Very rarely do researchers study all of the arrows in their model, but without the flow chart, it is difficult to see where the study fits into the big picture. We will also see that we can only determine the validity of most statistical analyses if we know where they fit into the flow chart.

Returning to our crayfish example, we see that the density of crayfish depends on several other variables. This justifies its designation as the "dependent variable" in statistical jargon. However, we also note that some of the other variables in the model (termed "independent variables") are in fact dependent on each other. This complicates our analysis. Some of the variables that directly affect crayfish density also have indirect effects because they influence other variables that can also affect crayfish density. For example, pollution directly affects crayfish, but it also indirectly affects crayfish through its effect on fish, which in turn affects crayfish.

Figure 2.4

There are statistical techniques for trying to untangle indirect effects and independent variables that are not really independent of each other (e.g., Chapter 10), but please do not skip to that chapter. Very rarely can we meet the assumptions of these analyses, and most of the researchers on your team will be focusing on limited parts of your flow chart.

Researchers use various methods to study individual parts (arrows). Some of these methods may not contribute data for a statistical analysis of the overall flow chart. Therefore, research planning by all team members has to be done in relation to the flow chart.

Figure 2.5

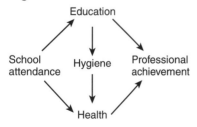

Three types of questions

IS IT REAL? The initial, and often the only, question in a study is whether an effect exists. This is the equivalent of asking whether we should include the arrow in our flow chart. This seems straightforward, but nothing is simple. A few scientists calculate the probability of the arrow's existence using Bayesian statistics. These statistics may be very useful for communicating with politicians and the general public. Albert (1997) gives a readable account of how Bayesian statistics can be used to answer simple questions. However, Bayesian statistics are not simple to understand or calculate (Moore 1997), and Guttman (1985) refers to them as "a cure worse than the disease."

Most statistical tests, statistics textbooks, and computer programs are based on frequentist techniques, which calculate the probability that the arrow does not exist. This is far from straightforward, and it is not the sort of probability that most nonscientists are comfortable with. The statistics that the members of your team will almost always use are based on Popperian philosophy (Chapter 5).

It is also important to realize that even the most powerful of the common statistical methods do not answer the question, "Does this effect normally exist?" Instead, they ask the question, "If all other variables were constant, would changing the value of this variable have an effect?" They therefore look at the direct effects, since indirect effects cannot be seen if the other variables are constrained as constant. This difference is not trivial. Some variables that have no direct effects on the response variables we are interested in are very important in the real world. Other variables that normally have only very small direct effects that are difficult to detect in the field, may have great potential in medicine or agriculture if their levels can be manipulated artificially.

The most convincing way of showing that a direct effect exists is through an experiment that manipulates the system so that only the variables being studied can influence the outcome. The results of such experiments are said to permit "strong inference" (see Platt 1964) as other confounding variables are eliminated. However, the results may not have much relevance to the real world (e.g., Carpenter 1999, Magnusson 2002a), and any factor a competent ecologist suggests is likely to have some effect (Tukey 1991, Johnson 1999).

> **The team leader and team members must be sure that the questions being asked by individual researchers are relevant to the overall goal.**

WHAT IS THE FORM AND MAGNITUDE OF THE EFFECT?   Finding out that an effect is different, or is not different, from zero is often not very useful (e.g., Rosenthal and Rubin 1994, Anderson et al. 2000). The second phase of research often asks questions about the form of a relationship that has been shown, or is assumed to exist. Most statistical models are built on simple linear or monotonic relationships, and our flow charts should reflect this. We might find that for every extra predatory fish in the system, we reduce the density of crayfish by three individuals per meter of stream. However, such a simple result is unlikely. Many ecological studies have shown that the effect of predators is not a simple linear function of predator den-

Figure 2.6

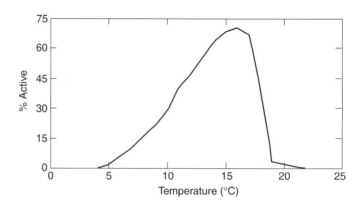

sity. Caughley and Sinclair (1994, refer to Chapter 11) give many examples. Low densities of crayfish may not be able to sustain populations of predatory fish. At high densities of crayfish, the predatory fish may be limited by factors other than food availability, such as the density of their own predators.

Many variables that affect biological processes behave in this way, having no effect at low levels, positive effects at intermediate levels, and negative effects at high levels. Figure 2.6 shows the relationship between temperature and the proportion of the population that is active for a hypothetical insect. You should think about how many relationships in your field have this form.

It is important to know the forms of the relationships between variables, as we usually have to add variables to our model, change the units of measurement (called transforming variables), or decide to investigate only a limited range of conditions, before we can proceed with most statistical or modeling techniques. In fact, it is obvious that we really need information about the form of the relationship before carrying out tests for the existence of an effect.

If we compared the level of insect activity at 5°C with that at 20°C, we would conclude that temperature has little or no effect on activity. However, if we compared the level of activity at 5°C with that at 15°C, we would conclude that temperature has a very large effect. This is a frequent problem when tests for the existence of a phenomenon have incorrect assumptions about the form of the relationship and the researcher has not investigated all of the likely levels of that phenomenon (Magnusson 2002a). We will consider this further in Chapters 7 and 11.

WHAT HAPPENS IF CONDITIONS CHANGE? Many researchers would like to answer the question, "How much effect does one variable have on another?" Unfortunately, the answer is usually, "It depends." To answer this question we must investigate the normal levels of the variable and its frequencies in the system (Petraitis et al.

1996, Magnusson 2002a). Therefore, the experimental manipulations recommend-ed for "strong inference" are usually not appropriate. In addition, when the effect of a variable depends on the levels of all the other "independent" variables, as occurs in the real world, there is no one correct answer.

Modelers usually do not try to make precise predictions, and they usually are not interested in the "strong inference" experiments. They try to simulate the workings of the system with a computer and simple mathematical relationships. By varying the level, and (or) the variability of each independent variable, and running their model hundreds or thousands of times, they try to determine which variables generally have the most effect on the outcome. If you have modelers on your team, you should discuss their needs early on because they can make little use of the types of data most researchers collect. Osenberg et al. (1999) give a good discussion of the difficulties of integrating studies even when all of the researchers were ostensibly studying the same simple question.

> **If the complexity of their statistics puts you off, consider designing the study to avoid, rather than repair, the errors.**

We have seen that researchers may have very different goals, even though they are apparently studying the same phenomenon. Some researchers try to achieve an intermediate solution. They not only collect data to infer the probability that an effect occurs and describe its usual form, they also obtain data needed by the mod-elers. They will probably be criticized by everyone (see Hairston 1989).

There is no one correct answer and science continues to advance spectacularly with different researchers working in different ways. However, for integrated studies, the team leader must know what sort of data collection and analysis each member of the team will undertake, and must make a judgment as to whether that data will be useful to other team members. Integrated sampling designs are often the most efficient, and we will consider some of them later. First, however, we must look at the scale of the question.

How Big Is Your Problem?

Many of the controversies in the scientific literature have occurred because re-searchers work on the same problem at different scales. The density of a species of plant may not be related to soil characteristics at a scale of tens of meters, even though soil characteristics explain much of the variation in density of plants among counties. At a larger scale, there may be no relationship between the pres-ence of the species on continents and the types of soils that occur on these continents. The answer to the question of whether soil affects the distribution of that species is "No, yes, no." Had we looked at other scales we may have obtained many other combinations of yes and no. It is therefore not surprising that readers of scientific literature become confused, and the general public even more so.

Allen and Starr (1982) give a series of photographs of a football game that show how the scale at which we observe a system determines what we can discover. When viewed from an aircraft, it is not possible to make any conclusions about the game, even though we can see the whole stadium. At a closer distance we can see the players but they are difficult to distinguish from the crowd in the background. At the next scale, it is possible to see the actions of the individual players and the progress of the game. At the smallest scale, from within the ball, the photograph is all black. Researchers think a lot about these aspects when they are planning to watch a football game. Surprisingly, they often give them little attention when planning scientific studies.

There is of course no universally correct scale for scientific studies. Many recent articles have discussed the importance of scale in science (see Peterson and Parker 1998, Lawton 1999, Pascual and Levin 1999, Petersen et al. 1999). Some of the most important scientific results have come from studies at tiny scales, and others from grand scales. However, in an integrated study, especially one designed to provide practical advice for politicians, there will be a limited range of scales appropriate to the overall aims of the study, and these are usually large (Bradshaw 1998, Ormerod et al. 1999).

> **To decide on a scale, you should first consider what area, population, time period, physical, chemical, or social situation you want the results to reflect.**

This is called your universe of interest. Potentially, all members of the team could work at similar scales, and presumably they have the same universe of interest. However, scientists tend to copy their sampling designs from recent publications in the specialist literature of their area. It may be difficult to convince a team member that they should use a particular sampling scale if a famous scientist, who has just published a study about the same organism in a prestigious journal, used a different scale of sampling. Although much is made of the pursuit of novelty in science, most scientists believe that their colleagues will criticize them if they challenge established dogma—and they are correct. In the worst case, the team member has to decide how much personal prestige they are willing to forgo for the good of the project.

Where to go from here?

Because researchers generally decide on a method of analysis copied from the literature before they consider the question, the analyses tend to define the questions rather than vice versa (Yoccoz 1991). It is therefore important that the team leader and the team members have some background in the concepts behind the types of analyses commonly used by scientists. Fortunately, all of the commonly used statistical methods are based on a few simple concepts. To use them, we have to be able to construct flow charts, interpret simple graphs, and understand the philosophy underlying statistical hypothesis tests.

The flow charts we constructed only show us where we think we are. They suggest the critical experiments or observations that we need. Platt (1964) said that we should "Devote half an hour to an hour to analytical thinking every day, writing out the logical tree and the alternatives and crucial experiments explicitly in a permanent notebook." Unfortunately, these skills are not taught in most statistics courses for ecologists. We will consider some of the basic aspects of these skills in the following chapters.

## CHAPTER 3

*"Statistics generally hide data,
instead of revealing them."*

Describing Things: Some "Scientific" Conventions and Some Useful Techniques

In this chapter we will discuss some simple statistics that are used to describe data or the populations from which they were obtained. Statistical techniques can help elucidate patterns hidden in the data if the model represented by our flow chart is complex, as we will see in Chapters 8 and 10. However, most statistical summaries found in the scientific literature relate to extremely simple situations in which the statistics generally hide data instead of revealing patterns. It is useful to know the terms so that you can read the literature and converse with your colleagues. However, only a few of the concepts will be important for the following chapters, and these are easily visualized in the form of simple graphs.

Consider how a researcher might describe the data they collected on crayfish densities in streams. Five streams were sampled and the data are presented as the number of crayfish per 100 meters of stream. The data could be shown as a list of densities (1, 3, 4, 5, 7 animals per 100 m of stream). However, such data are often presented with other data for comparison (see Chapters 5 and 6). Therefore, we consider how they can be presented to their best advantage. The simplest method would be to graph them (Figure 3.1).

The graph takes up more space, but allows us to instantly evaluate the general value of the data (mean), and the variability around the mean. Most researchers have an intuitive feel for what the mean represents, but not the various statistical descriptors of variability. Most lay people use the range (the difference between the highest and lowest numbers) to describe the variability, but this has the disadvantage that it only uses information from two of the five points.

A slightly more complex but still intuitively obvious way to describe the variability is to use the mean absolute deviation, which is the mean of the distances of all the points from the mean. Figure 3.2 shows these distances, except for the distance of the point with the value "4," which is zero distance from the mean. We can summarize the data by saying that the mean equals 4 and the mean absolute deviation equals 1.66. We use the absolute deviation because the sum of the deviations, which are negative below and positive above the mean, is zero.

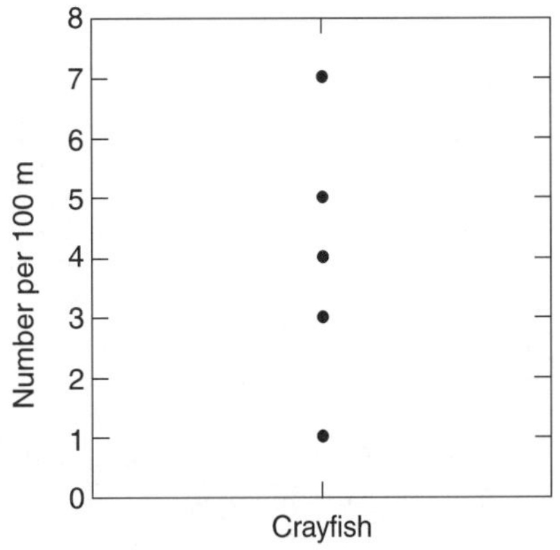

With a little practice, most researchers can look at a graph and quickly estimate where one mean absolute deviation either side of the mean lies. One might therefore expect this descriptor to often be used to describe data. Nevertheless, it is rarely used, and another descriptor, the standard deviation, or a derivation of it, is used instead. The standard deviation, although far from intuitive, has advantages related to some more complicated analyses that we will consider in later chapters.

Between one and three times a year, for the last ten years, we have asked classes of graduate students and researchers to indicate where one standard deviation each side of the mean would lie on simple graphs like Figure 3.1. Very few of them came close to the right position, and of those who did, almost none could explain why they chose those positions. Many of the students and researchers had published standard deviations to describe their data. It is therefore a little worrying that they did not know what they had described. They were also unable to interpret the results of other researchers who used the same descriptor.

The standard deviation and related statistics are used so often that it is worthwhile to spend a little time trying to visualize what they represent. Remember however, that there are a number of other descriptors of spread that may be more appropriate in many situations (Iglewicz 1983). Rather than absolute deviations from the mean, standard deviations and related statistics are based on squared deviations from the mean. If we sum the squared deviations from the mean, we get an estimate of a quantity called the sum of squares (SS). This is not very useful for describing variability because, being a sum, it increases with every extra observation. However, if we take the mean of the squared deviations we have a

Figure 3.1

Figure 3.2

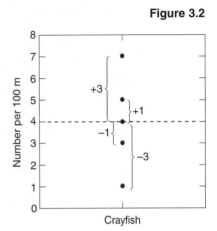

Figure 3.3

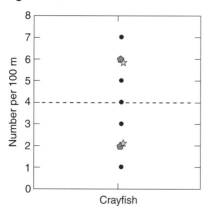

Crayfish

descriptor that does not depend on sample size. This is called the variance.

Unlike the mean absolute deviation, the mean squared deviation (variance) is not useful for describing variability because it probably won't even fit on our graph. The variance of the data in Figure 3.1 is 4! To get it back onto the scale of the original measurements, we take its square root. The square root of the mean of the squared deviations is called the standard deviation. This seems a circuitous route to get a value that is different from, but not very different from, the mean absolute deviation.

The values of one mean absolute deviation either side of the mean (see the stars in Figure 3.3), and one standard deviation either side of the mean (see the pentagons in Figure 3.3) are almost identical. Both deviations were calculated for a population rather than a sample. We will not discuss the difference here, as the difference for graphical interpretation is trivial except in the case of extremely small sample sizes. We will discuss the uses of standard deviations later, but for now it is enough for you to realize that the value of the standard deviation is not usually very different from the mean absolute deviation. Therefore, you can visualize the approximate positions of one standard deviation either side of the mean on a graph. This should help you understand other researchers' descriptions of their data.

We have been talking about descriptors of data. As the data are usually samples taken from larger populations, we are only describing the sample. Such sample descriptors, called statistics, are often used as estimates of the real descriptors of the populations, called parameters. Some authors use the terminology a little differently but, in general, parameters are characteristics of populations, and statistics are estimates of parameters based on samples. Note that when we refer to statistical populations we are referring to populations of numbers, which may or may not be related to biological populations. The population of heights of men has a mean much higher than the population of heights of women, but when we refer to human populations we are referring to populations that consist of about half men and half women. Conversely, the mean height of a species of antelope may be the same as the mean height of men, but this does not imply that men and antelopes belong to the same biological population.

The standard deviation is a useful parameter for describing the variability in a number of measurements if the population of measurements has a frequency distribution that conforms to a theoretical distribution called the "normal." In that case, about 68% of the population lies within one standard deviation of the mean, and about 95% of the population lies within two standard deviations of the mean. If the distribution is not normal, the standard deviation is quite useless for describing the variability in the population (Mosteller and Tukey 1968), a fact that appears to have been forgotten by most researchers.

We can also calculate the standard deviations of parameters, which are called standard errors. When authors refer to the standard error without specifying a parameter, they are referring to the standard error of the mean. To illustrate this, we used a random number generator to produce 300 measurements from a distribution with the same mean and standard deviation as the data in Figure 3.2. We then took 60 samples of five, giving 60 means, each based on a sample of five. The first sample is illustrated beside the 60 means in Figure 3.4. Its mean is shown as the black circle among the other means.

The sample's mean (2.4) is quite different from the true mean of 4.0. However, the mean of the 60 means (3.8) is closer. Obviously, the mean of 60 samples contains much more information than a single sample of five. With 60 means, we can also estimate the standard deviation of the means (standard error) fairly accurately. The standard deviation of the 60 means is 0.77. Therefore, we expect about 68% of the means taken from that population to lie within 4 ± 0.77.

The distribution of the means tends to be normal even if the distribution of the measurements in the original population is not. This is a consequence of the central limit theorem, and is the justification for using statistical tests based on the normal distribution even when the population of measurements does not have a normal distribution.

If all of these means of means and parameters of parameters are getting a bit confusing, don't worry about it. We do not use these concepts very much except to see how some researchers present their data, and how they could present it more simply and effectively. Nobody takes 60 samples to work out a standard error because the statisticians tell us that we can estimate the standard error from a single sample. There is a different standard error for every sample size that we can take. However, a single sample of five can theoretically estimate the standard deviation of the means based on a very large number of samples of five.

The magic formula says to just divide the estimate of the population standard deviation based on the sample by the square root of the number of observations in the sample. In our case, we know that the standard error of means of samples of five is about 0.77. Figure 3.5 shows the distribution of the 60 estimates of the standard error based on our 60 samples. We listed the standard error based on the standard deviation of the 60 means as

Figure 3.4

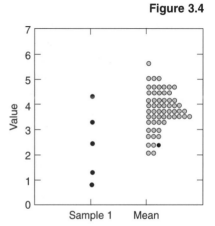

Figure 3.5

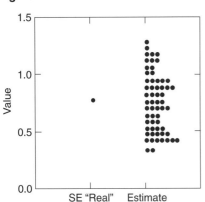

"real" because it will be very close to the real standard error, which is unknown.

Obviously, estimates of the standard errors based on samples of five are very imprecise. Many of the estimates are very far from the best estimate. The larger the sample size, the better the estimates obtained by the magic formula. However, to a statistician, they are rarely easier to interpret than a graph showing the raw data, and most researchers have little idea what they represent. It is possible to infer confidence intervals based on the size of the estimated standard error and the sample size.

Students incorrectly interpret a 95% confidence interval to mean that there is a 95% chance that the true parameter lies within the interval. From the point of view of classical statistics, this statement is meaningless. Either the true mean lies in the interval or not. The correct interpretation of Neyman confidence intervals (Neyman 1937) is that if the series of experiments is repeated many times, and a confidence interval is calculated for each one, about 95% of the calculated confidence intervals would include the true mean (Bard 1974). However, the standard confidence intervals are only valid if they are applied to all data. If the confidence intervals are applied only after a statistical test indicates "significance," as is standard practice, the confidence intervals given in textbooks are too small (Meeks and D'Agostino 1983).

Few researchers understand these concepts. In any case, most standard errors are presented on graphs with no indication of the sample size in the legend (Magnusson 2000). Often there are different sample sizes in different parts of the graph. These demonstrate scientific culture, but communicate little else. In the following section we illustrate different methods of presenting data on graphs. We leave it to you to decide which best convey information about the data obtained. First, we consider a graph showing data with a small sample size (Figure 3.6).

Figure 3.6A shows the data that were collected on crayfish densities in different rivers. Figure 3.6B shows some statistical summaries commonly used on graphs. These are based on the same data shown in Figure 3.6A. The standard deviation (SD) is dissimilar to the standard error (SE), but not very different from the 95% confidence interval (95% CI) of the mean. If you are not certain that you and your audience will understand the implications of the three different statistical summaries, show them the data.

Figure 3.6A is called a dispersion graph. Such graphs can present a surprising amount of information. Figure 3.7A is a dispersion graph of data collected by a researcher from 40 rivers with fish and 40 rivers without fish. This graph is a little difficult to interpret because some points obscure others. In Figure 3.7B, we off-

(A)

(B)

Figure 3.6

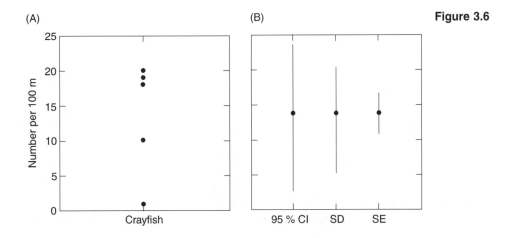

set the points. This graph is technically a dot histogram but, in terms of communication, it can be considered a dispersion graph with the points offset so as not to obscure each other.

   Note that these graphs show just about all of the data collected in the study, but many scientists do not consider them "scientific." After all, anybody, even non-scientists, could evaluate them. Team members prefer graphs that display their scientific culture, even if these distort the information. (Hall [1959] gives many examples of the danger of letting culture make decisions for us.) Figure 3.8A illustrates a bar graph of the same data presented in Figure 3.7. The error bars represent standard errors. This type of graph effectively hides all of the information about the amount of data that we collected.

(A)

(B)

Figure 3.7

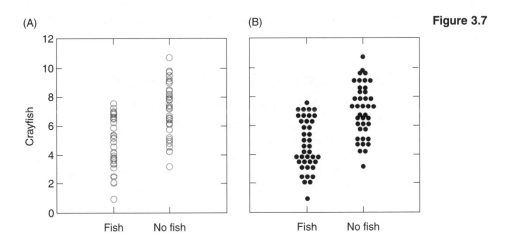

Figure 3.8   (A)   (B)

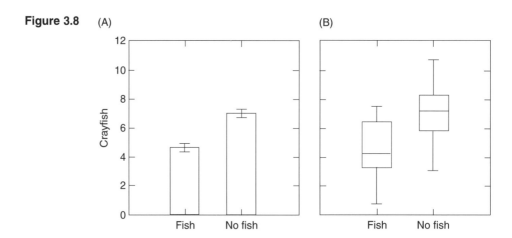

Would-be statisticians will say that they can interpret the error bars because their assumptions about the real-world are always correct. Besides that, any competent biologist has an intuitive feel for what a standard error represents, and should be able to reconstitute the original graph in their head. However, we have taught statistics to graduate and post-graduate students and consulted for practicing researchers during a combined period equivalent to more than two decades, and we can assure you that neither of those assertions is true. If you want to hide your data, put them in a bar graph.

Box plots, such as Figure 3.8B, are marginally better at showing data. However, few researchers know how to interpret them, and we have still lost the information about how much data we used to produce the plot. Box plots are a good alternative when you have so much data that they cannot be reasonably presented on a dispersion graph (Tukey 1972), but they are useless for planning sampling. Use them as a last resort but never as the standard method of presenting results, hypothetical or not.

How to Give a False Impression with a Computer

It is important to remember that some measures of variability generated by the computer may not be the ones that you are interested in. There are methods of calculating standard errors based on line transects (e.g., Krebs 1998). However, remember that standard errors based on such distance methods estimate the standard error of the transect. This estimates the variability expected if you repeat that transect. It tells you nothing about the expected standard error if you had replicate transects within the area of interest; this has to be estimated by other methods (Caughley and Sinclair 1994).

Primatologists frequently give the standard error of densities of monkeys in a reserve based on one or two transects. This information is meaningless (Magnusson 2001). They confuse the variability of repeated sampling of that transect with the variability among transects. The method would be approximately valid if the transect was so long that it sampled almost the whole reserve. Yet, this would be very inefficient. When you present a measure of variability you must ensure that it refers to your universe of interest.

A related problem is the estimation of standard errors in population size by mark-recapture (Abuabara and Petrere 1997, Krebs 1998). These methods estimate the number of individuals in the population that are susceptible to capture. To convert this to a density is complicated unless the population occupies a discrete area, and all animals in the population are susceptible to capture (Anderson et al. 1983, Parmenter et al. 2003). Animals often vary range sizes seasonally or inter-annually due to variation in resources. The estimate of population size and its standard error may be statistically correct, but most ecologists are interested in estimates of density, not the size of the trappable population. If you do not understand the difference, do not use these methods.

In this chapter, we were concerned with statistical summaries. We use some of this terminology in later chapters, where variation is often expressed as sums of squares or variances. However, you do not have to be able to visualize these quantities in order to use them.

> **The other statistical summaries are rarely useful, except to show your academic culture, and they should only be used when tables or dispersion graphs are not a viable alternative.**

Do not worry if you don't understand statistical summaries, few researchers do. They are like the King's clothes, and only the very honest will admit, "I can't see them."

## CHAPTER 4

"Deciding how much is adequate, but not wasteful, is the art of the scientist."

How Much Evidence Is Enough?

Our artist painting a landscape does not use a canvas that is too big to fit in a room. The artist also does not try to tell a story in ten different ways on the same canvas. If the artist wants to communicate, and not die of hunger before the work is completed, the artist must decide when to stop painting. Deciding what is adequate, but not wasteful, is the art of the painter. It is also the art of the scientist. Consider a simple question and a simple graph.

Our scientist studying crayfish decides to test whether locations with no predatory fish have more crayfish than locations with predatory fish. The number of crayfish in sections of stream with predatory fish and without predatory fish is counted, but the scientist is unsure how many sections to sample. Obviously, one sample of each type of section will not reveal much (Figure 4.1A). Therefore, the sample number is increased to three of each type of section, but the scientist still has doubts (Figure 4.1B). The sample number is increased to five sections of stream in each category and the scientist no longer has much doubt (Figure 4.1C).

The "dummy data collection" as named by Dytham (1999) seems very simple, yet it is one of the most powerful means of planning research. Connolly et al. (2001) called the process a "thought experiment." There are some very elegant mathematical formulas for deciding how many observations are needed to detect an effect of a given magnitude (e.g., Krebs 1989). However, all require preliminary samples, and most only apply to fairly simple situations. Generally, asking an experienced researcher to make hypothetical graphs that show the expected variability in the data is as reliable as any of the computer methods. Just keep adding points until the graphs look convincing.

Figure 4.1

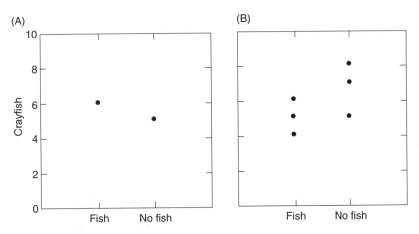

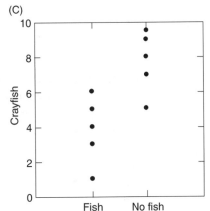

If you cannot extract useful information about the scale of the project from team members, there are a few "fly by the seat of the pants" rules that you can use. Ecological data usually show the sort of variability given in Figure 4.1. Therefore, for comparisons between categories, you should be sure that there are at least four observations per category, and preferably more. However, there is usually no point in having more than 10 observations per category unless data are very cheap to collect, or you think it important to detect extremely small differences between categories. We will add other "fly by the seat of the pants" rules in the following chapters, but four observations per category generally stand us in good stead.

How Good Is Your Information?

To answer the question, "How much information is enough?" we must also ask, "What is the quality of the information?"

This is important because our statistical questions must reflect our biological questions.

In the early 1980's, Stuart Hurlbert alerted the world to errors in most ecological analyses and called these errors pseudoreplication. Replicates are what statisticians call independent observations. Generally, you expect the amount of information you have to increase with the number of observations, but this is not always so.

When a new observation merely provides the same information obtained in previous observations it does not increase the total amount of knowledge available to us, and it may fool us into believing that we have more information than we really do. Because the new observation was not a true replicate, in the sense of providing more information, Hurlbert coined it a "pseudoreplicate," which means "false replicate."

Hurlbert (1984) provided many simple examples of pseudoreplication, but let's consider our crayfish study. What if our biologist samples five sections of one stream without predatory fish, and five sections of another stream with predatory fish? All of the first stream may have fewer crayfish because of lower productivity, pollution, epidemic disease, or any one of a multitude of factors known to affect crayfish. One observation of crayfish density in a stream is obviously not independent of other observations in the same stream. Therefore the five observations do not carry five times more information than a single observation.

This simple error pervades scientific literature. Kruskal (1988) provides examples of non-independence in situations that have nothing to do with science. Everything is connected to everything else, and it can be extremely difficult to determine whether any observation is truly independent. The artistry of great scientists is shown in their ability to collect observations that are truly independent in relation to their questions; and that is a rare quality. Therefore, members of a research team have to make sure that the observations being made by other members are not pseudoreplicates in terms of the global question.

This is a difficult task because no observation is inherently valid or invalid.

A pseudoreplicate for one question may be a valid replicate for another. For instance, had our biologist been interested in differences in densities of crayfish between the two rivers, and only these two rivers, the five observations in each river may have been perfectly valid replicates, each one bringing more information about the density of crayfish in one of the rivers.

Pseudoreplication can be spatial, temporal, phylogenetic, or technical. We discussed one example of spatial pseudoreplication and Hurlbert (1984) gives many more. Spatial pseudoreplication is the most common, but also the most easily avoided form of pseudoreplication. Team members justify it on the basis of logistic difficulties, but the time and money that get lost when the sampling devices are transported from one site to the next are usually more than compensated for by the strong conclusions that can be made from the high quality evidence that gets collected over a larger, and more appropriate, spatial scale.

Temporal pseudoreplication is often harder to detect, and harder to avoid. It occurs because the state of a system cannot change instantaneously. If a tree produces fruit in a month with high rainfall, it will probably continue to produce fruit in the next month, and the rainfall in that next month will probably still be high. It therefore appears that there is an association between high rainfall and monthly fruit production, even though the flowering event that triggered the start of fruiting may have occurred many months before, in the dry season. For this reason, the causes of "seasonality" cannot be demonstrated at a single site in a single season.

Either many decades of work at a single site, or studies of many sites with different weather patterns are necessary to determine the causes of seasonality. Despite this, many team members will want to study seasonality because they believe that it is so obvious that they must be able to find "significant" effects. The causes of temporal variation are extremely difficult to study (see Powell and Steele 1995, von Ende 1993) and the team members should seek statistical advice from a specialist before including studies of temporal variation in the overall objective.

Phylogenetic pseudoreplication is a very complex topic that is mainly, though not always, a problem when species are the units being sampled. Interested readers can consult Garland et al. (1992) for an introduction to the literature. Studies of seeds, tadpoles, and insect larvae often suffer from phylogenetic pseudoreplication because the organisms used in experiments are closely related. Seeds from a single tree, tadpoles from a single egg clutch, or insect larvae found at a particular locality are often very similar because of genetic or maternal provisioning effects, and they usually do not present the range of responses seen in the larger population. Rather than try to correct for phylogenetic effects in such studies it is usually best to try to collect unrelated individuals for experiments. If the scale of the sampling is appropriate for the question, this will happen naturally.

Technical pseudoreplication occurs because different observers or instruments are used for different parts of the experiment. When undetected, this comes under Hurlbert's "demonic intrusion," but there is little excuse for it in most well-planned experiments. Occasionally, equipment failure or ill health makes changes unavoidable. In these cases, it may be that an honest statement of the possibility of technical pseudoreplication is needed, so readers can make their own assessment.

Returning to our simple graph, the effect of pseudoreplication is to reduce the number of usable points on the graph. When only two rivers are sampled, all of the points within the ovals in Figure 4.2A describe the same object, and reduce to the two points in Figure 4.2B. Few biologists, many fewer statisticians, and no computers will be able to recognize that most of the information in Figure 4.2A is useless for understanding our initial question.

Data are only useful when they provide information.

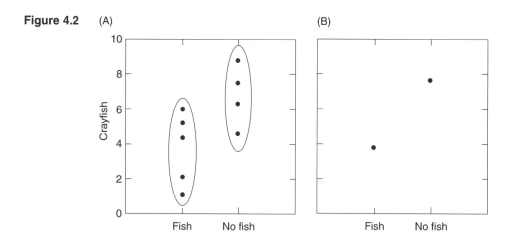

Figure 4.2

If our graphs are misleading, our analyses will be misleading, and we will not have made an honest appraisal of the evidence.

There are some statistical techniques we can use to take into account the fact that not all of the observations are independent (e.g., nested analysis of variance), but these are only useful if the researcher can recognize the lack of independence and inform the statistician or the computer. None of them are as powerful as recognizing the pseudoreplication and redesigning the sampling regime to avoid it.

To decide how much evidence is enough, we must consider how many points we have to put on each graph, and then make sure that the points are independent; in other words, that each point represents independent information about our question. You do not have to be a statistician, or even a biologist to do this, and the process is remarkably simple. However, because much published science skips this simple first step, results are difficult to interpret and may even be misleading. We will jump ahead to consider pseudoreplication in relation to a statistical test that almost everyone has heard of, the Chi-square test of a contingency table.

Contingency table analysis is almost never appropriate for answering ecological questions (Hurlbert 1984, Magnusson 1999a), and this relates to what an independent observation actually is in relation to the question.

A biologist studying the diet of fish researches whether the diet of adult fish is different from that of juvenile fish. The results of this study can be found in Table 4.1, which compares the number of copepods and algae found in juvenile and adult fish.

The biologist knows that it is impossible to publish results without a statistical test and so a contingency table analysis is applied which results in the following mathematical hieroglyphics $\chi^2_1 = 6030$, $P << 0.001$. Do not worry if you do not know what these hieroglyphics mean. Most readers will revise what they think

Table 4.1	Copepods	Algae
Adults	3217	18
Juveniles	23	2936

they mean after reading a few more chapters of this book. The important thing to know is that most practicing ecologists interpret these results to mean that it is very unlikely that juveniles and adults have the same diet. However, this interpretation changes when we look at the biologist's notebook (Table 4.2).

According to Table 4.2, it is apparent that there is not a convincing general difference between the diets of adults and juveniles. What if, by chance, an adult swims into a school of copepods, and one juvenile gorges on plankton? Why did the test give us a false answer? Because the analysis assumed that each register of a copepod or alga was independent of the others. The data did not reflect contingency.

Table 4.2	Copepods	Algae
Adult 1	0	6
Adult 2	3211	7
Adult 3	6	5
Juvenile 1	8	2906
Juvenile 2	8	1
Juvenile 3	7	29

A valid test could have been carried out had one item from each fish's gut been randomly selected and the rest of the sample from that gut discarded. This would have required 6194 individual fish, each taken from a different school. Obviously, that would have been a very inefficient way of answering the question. It is because contingency table analyses require independent observations, and only accumulate information in the form of presence or absence, that they are so inefficient for most ecological questions. There are some applications in which it is appropriate to work with categories, but the best and most intuitive models use continuous rather than categorical variables. Friendly (1995) gives a simple explanation based on an analogy of gas molecules in a chamber.

> **When you see a contingency table analysis you can assume, with some certainty, that the researcher used pseudoreplication and the statistical inferences are meaningless.**

However, there is a small chance that the analysis was correct and the experimental design was very inefficient. There is an even smaller chance that the contingency table analysis is appropriate for the question. Now you can see why "basic" statistics courses often only look at the probability of taking a certain proportion of black balls from one barrel. Barrels do not replicate, they do not swim in schools, and they do not change much over time. Therefore, they are easy to model mathematically. However, they might not have much relevance for most ecologists.

The best way to avoid pseudoreplication is to draw a conceptual map of the distribution of the objects you are interested in. Each point on the diagram should represent a potential sampling unit. The sampling unit will have a name relevant to the discipline. It may be called a plot, focal group, grain, pixel, or something else. Sampling units are often related to area, but may also be related to time intervals, species, experimental units, or other objects. They are always the smallest measurable unit that still has meaning to the research.

The diagram should cover the entire universe of interest. This might be called the universe of inference, scale of inference, scope, frame, etc., depending on the discipline. The distribution of sampling units will reveal the universe of sampling, also called the scale of the experiment, scope of experiment, scale, extent, image, etc. The diagrams do not have to be accurate or artistic; they serve only to convey a general impression.

Two real examples illustrate the technique: A student wanted to compare the behavior of birds in Amazonian and Central Brazilian savannas. Many individuals were studied, but when the savannas of interest were mapped (Figure 4.3A is a conceptual representation of that map), it became apparent to the student that the sampling universe was not the same as the universe of interest and the question was changed. Note that this simple conceptual map, with ovals representing areas of savannas, a straight line representing the boundary between biomes, and three black dots representing sampling areas, is quite adequate to show that the

Figure 4.3

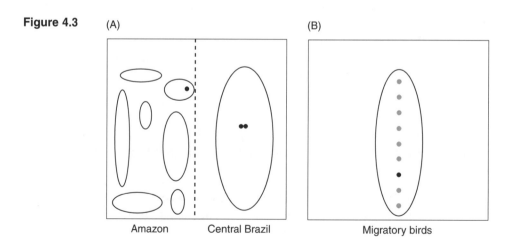

(A)

Amazon   Central Brazil

(B)

Migratory birds

universe of sampling does not correspond to the universe of interest in the original question.

Figure 4.3B shows the universe of interest for a student studying migratory birds. The student wanted to make inferences about long distance migration in wading birds. Even though there were a large number of birds, only one of the species that showed that form of migration (the black dot) was sampled. The simple diagram, with species of interest represented by a line of circles, shows how restricted the universe of sampling was in relation to the universe of interest. The student realized that before making any strong inferences the question had to be restricted to one species, or the number of species sampled had to be increased. Generally speaking, conceptual maps will give you a good idea of whether you should treat the data as a hint (no real replication), as a strong inference (lots of independent evidence), or something in between. What appears to be mapping the sampling units is really the process of mapping out the question.

> **In the following chapters, we discuss how most of the common statistical analyses can be regarded as methods of reducing complex problems to two dimensions so the results can be presented in simple dispersion graphs.**

If team members cannot represent the expected results of their analyses in simple graphical form, they do not understand the analyses and should not be using them. However, when confronted with their inability to produce two-dimensional graphical representations of their results, team members claim that the role of scientists is not to produce simple graphs that can be understood by everyone. They say that the objective of a scientific study is to produce probability statements. Therefore, in the next chapter, we consider the unusual definition of probability used by most scientists.

## CHAPTER 5

"Popper's basic thesis was that you cannot prove anything, only disprove it."

When Highly Improbable Means Very Likely

Statisticians have been using a rather counterintuitive definition of probability for a long time (Platt 1964), but its general acceptance can be traced to Sir Karl Popper whose research spanned the early decades of the twentieth century. Popper was an Austrian, so it is surprising to learn that the Queen of England awarded him the title of Knight. His philosophy had wide reaching ramifications in politics, the social sciences, and in learning theory. However, most scientists do not realize this, and they use Popper's philosophy as a cold-hearted arbiter for an "objective" world.

Popper's basic thesis is that you cannot prove anything, only disprove it. To really understand the thesis you need to read much more than we can provide in this text. Those interested in a colorful, though long-winded tour through recent history should read Popper's (1976) *Unended Quest: An Intellectual Autobiography*. Those with less time could look at Magee's (1982) *Popper*.

In the political world, Popper dismantled the Nazi's scientific justification for genocide (hence his knighthood). In many ways, his ideas on how humans learn presaged the modern field of sociobiology. Popperian philosophy is the basis of the "decision tree" approach to planning studies, which has been touted as one of the most powerful in science (Platt 1964). His philosophy is the underpinning of almost all modern statistical textbooks and it is this philosophy that we will consider here. However, Popperian philosophy, and especially the frequentist approach, is not the only or necessarily the best scientific method. Pickett et al. (1994) offer a good introduction to some other statistical ways of looking at the world.

Hilborn and Mangel (1997) wrote a very good book, *The Ecological Detective*, which gives an overview of means of investigating ecological phenomena and contrasts several "different" approaches to research. Rather than consider the different research agendas as different approaches, we consider them as differences in emphasis. Although Hilborn and Mangel (1997) were loathe to call their models "hypotheses," and taught a Bayesian paradigm, they began their discussion with the assumption that the reader already knew just about everything we are presenting in this book. We recommend that teachers read Hilborn and Mangel's book before giving a course in statistics, and that students read their book after reading this one.

Popper believed that we learn by being wrong. Consider a newborn baby. It is programmed to expect something about the world. Without a program in its brain it would be like a computer with no software—totally dead. Let us imagine that the baby is programmed to believe that the world is smooth (this is hypothetical as the authors must admit that they do not remember back that far). The baby's parents have been careful to make sure that all the things it touches within the first few days of life are smooth. Every time it touches something it can find no reason to reject its preconception that the whole world is smooth. Note, however, that it does not matter how many smooth objects it touches; it never proves that the world is smooth.

All it takes is one rough object, perhaps a rough blue toy that its older brother threw into the cradle, in order for the baby to reject its conjecture that the whole world is smooth. The baby discovers that it was wrong and creates another conjecture, perhaps that all things in the world except for blue objects are smooth. The baby will only advance when it has reason to disprove that conjecture, and create new ones based on new information.

This example illustrates the fact that it is very easy to obtain evidence to disprove something; often a single observation will do. However, no amount of corroboration can prove that a general conjecture is correct. Popperian statistics exploit this line of reasoning, though the line of reasoning used in most conventional statistics books is much more restrictive, and is generally called "frequentist." Practitioners of conventional (frequentist) statistics do not ask what the probability is that they are right; they ask what the probability is that they are wrong. To do this they have to set up a "scarecrow" (or decoy). This "straw man" is called the null hypothesis.

> **A null hypothesis is a statement about how the world would be if our conjecture is wrong.**

Earlier we conjectured that the presence of predatory fish affects crayfish density and our graph was consistent with that conjecture. Our null hypothesis is that

Figure 5.1

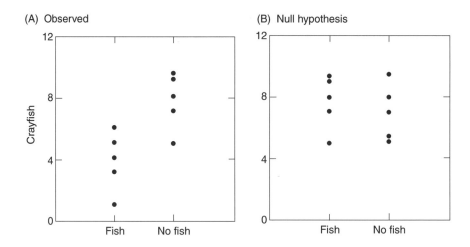

(A) Observed

(B) Null hypothesis

the graph is consistent with there being no difference between streams with predatory fish and fishless streams. Figure 5.1A illustrates our initial graph, constructed under the hypothesis that fish affect crayfish densities. Figure 5.1B illustrates what the graph would look like if the null hypothesis, that there is no difference between streams with fish and streams without fish, were correct.

The art of the scientist is to be able to visualize the graph representing the null hypothesis and compare this to the graph obtained from the data. However, there are many graphs that represent the null hypothesis. We could sample 10 different streams and the result would be slightly different. Dealing with lots of different possibilities under the null hypothesis is what inferential statistics is all about.

We obviously cannot fit too many graphs on a page, so we will look at just one thing on each graph to make the comparison. That one measurement from each graph is called a statistic. We have to do some sums here, but they are very simple. For our observed data (see Figure 5.1A) we calculate the difference between the mean value of crayfish density in fishless and fish-present streams. For these data, the difference between the mean density of crayfish in fishless streams (7.7) and in fish-present streams (3.8) is 3.9. We call our statistic "DIF" and, for the observed data DIF = –3.9. For the hypothetical data in Figure 5.1B, the difference between the mean density of crayfish in fishless streams (7.7) and in fish-present streams (7.0) is 0.7 (i.e., DIF = 0.7).

This is intuitive. When predatory fish affect crayfish densities, we expect a much larger mean difference between fish and fishless streams than when they don't. However, a cynic may say that the association between crayfish density and the presence of fish is accidental. By sampling only five streams, we may have selected five streams with fish that by chance had a lower mean density than the fishless streams. We can see that the critic may have a point. If just one stream has no crayfish, and it happens to fall in the fish-present category, it would lower the overall mean for that category.

Table 5.1

Stream	Fish	Crayfish	FISH 1	FISH 2	FISH 3
1	+	1	+	+	+
2	–	5	–	+	–
3	+	3	+	+	+
4	–	7	–	–	–
5	+	4	+	–	–
6	–	8	+	–	+
7	+	5	–	–	–
8	–	9	+	–	+
9	+	6	–	+	+
10	–	9.5	–	+	–

To evaluate this argument, we need to create a more specific hypothesis about our observed result. Let's say that we expect there to be a difference between fish-present and fishless streams in our sample, and that the difference will be greater than expected for a random association between crayfish density and fish presence. The null hypothesis says that we still expect a difference between fish-present and fishless streams in our sample, but that the difference will be about as big as expected for a random association between crayfish density and fish presence.

The question now is "How big does DIF have to be before we can reject the null hypothesis?" (and by default, continue to believe in our hypothesis). To answer this, we need to calculate DIF when the null hypothesis is true, and to do this we will flip a coin to randomly assign the status of fish-present (heads) or fishless (tails) to the values of crayfish density that we measured (Table 5.1). The variables FISH 1, FISH 2, and FISH 3 are created by tossing a coin, with the further restriction of only five of each type of stream (FISH ±) so that there are the same number of fish-present and fishless streams as in the original sample.

In Table 5.1, columns two (Fish) and three (Crayfish) show the observed data used to construct Figure 5.1A, and columns FISH 1, FISH 2, and FISH 3 are our random allocation of fish status to streams. We use these columns and the original data on crayfish density to create graphs of the expected results when the null hypothesis of a random allocation of fish status to each stream is true (Figure 5.2A–C).

We calculate DIF for each of these graphs. The first has a DIF = –0.5, the second has a DIF = –0.75, and the third has a DIF = 1.375. If we graphed more of these expected results when the null hypothesis is true, how likely are we to encounter a graph with a DIF as big or bigger than the absolute value of the one we calculated for the observed data (–3.9)? To answer this we need many more graphs and ran-

Figure 5.2

(A)

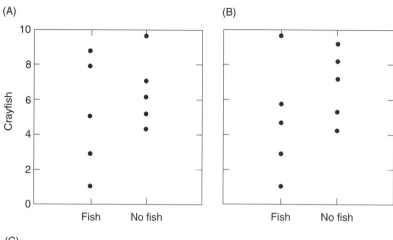

(C)

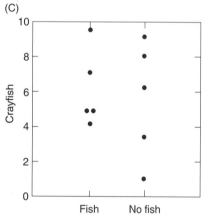

domly allocating (by flipping coins) fish status to streams is inefficient. Fortunately, computers can simulate the process very efficiently, so we programmed our computer to calculate 100 DIFs based on the random allocation of the presence of fish to the streams. Table 5.2 gives the first 20 DIFs the computer calculated.

When the null hypothesis is true, the first 20 results have a smaller absolute value than the DIF of –3.9 that we calculated for the observed data, but there are a lot of possibilities we have not considered for the null hypothesis. If we make a graph to compare the observed DIF to the 100 DIFs calculated when the null hypothesis was true (Figure 5.3), we find that only two of them have an absolute value as large as our observed value.

We therefore conclude that there are approximately two chances in 100 of obtaining an absolute value of DIF as big as 3.9 when there is no association between the presence of fish and the density of crayfish. We considered only the absolute values of the results because we asked a general question about whether fish affected crayfish density. This is called a two-tailed test. Had we only been asking whether fish decrease crayfish density, we could have carried out a more sensitive, one-tailed test by counting only how many simulated results were less than or equal to –3.9. However, the principle is the same and we do not want to get lost in details here.

We should review the steps we followed because they are general for all inferential tests. Similar processes are advocated by most authors (e.g., Huberty 1987).

Step 1. Visualize the expected result when the hypothesis you are testing is correct.

Step 2. Visualize the expected result when the hypothesis you are testing is incorrect. This result must derive from a process that is antithetical to your hypothesis, and that process is called the null hypothesis.

Step 3. Create a measurement that reflects the difference between results expected in Step 1 and Step 2. This measurement is called a statistic.

Step 4. Obtain many values of the statistic using a process in which the null hypothesis is true (i.e., when your hypothesis is wrong).

Step 5. Compare the value of the statistic for the observed data with the values of the statistic calculated when the null hypothesis was true (null values). Then use the proportion of the null values equal to or greater than the observed value as an indication of the probability of obtaining the observed value when the null hypothesis is true.

Step 6. Make a decision as to whether that probability is so small that you can reject the null hypothesis, and continue believing in your hypothesis (note that you never prove your hypothesis correct, even if you reject the null hypothesis).

If this seems complicated, return to Figure 5.1. Please note the process we just used, and will continue to use, throughout this book. We had a complex question involving one hundred graphs. We used some simple math to calculate a measure of what we were interested in (in this case a difference), and used the resulting values to create a simple, single graph that allows us to make a decision.

Even the convoluted logic of Popperian philosophy can be represented on a simple graph.

Table 5.2

Graph	DIF	Graph	DIF
1	2.70	11	2.1
2	1.90	12	2.7
3	−0.09	13	−3.1
4	2.50	14	1.5
5	−2.70	15	−1.1
6	1.70	16	−0.1
7	0.50	17	1.3
8	1.10	18	−0.5
9	1.50	19	−0.7
10	3.10	20	−0.3

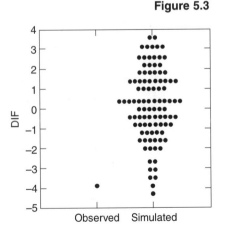

Figure 5.3

It should now be obvious why scientists look for low probabilities. They are basically asking whether they are wrong, and only accept that they might be right if the probability that they are wrong is small. To do this they must create a hypothesis that represents all the ways they might be wrong. Much of the disagreement in the scientific literature stems from disagreements as to what the null hypothesis is, how to measure it, and whether the available evidence is sufficient to reject it or not. A good sampling design usually has only one logical interpretation. With bad designs, there are many alternative interpretations and few conclusions can be reached with confidence.

How Textbooks Tell the Story

The story we just told is fairly simple once you get used to Popperian logic. However, statistics books usually manage to leave the reader with the impression that something much more complex was done. Part of the problem is historical, and part is due to the unnecessary inversion of graphs. You do not have to read the following section unless you want to know how our simple graphs relate to what you may see in other textbooks. To understand the differences, we consider the analysis most frequently used to determine whether two samples are different, the Student's t-test.

The student's real name was William S. Gosset, and he worked for a brewery. Therefore, he was interested in practical, as well as theoretical results. Gosset's null hypothesis was a little different from the one we used for our coin-tossing test. He asked, "What is the probability of two different samples being drawn from a common population of measurements?" The logic of this is obvious. Two samples drawn randomly from the same population can only be different because of chance. Gosset asked, "With what frequency can we expect samples with means as different as those in our sample if they indeed come from a common population of measurements?"

Gosset's null hypothesis is similar to ours in that it asks whether some process other than chance is likely to result in differences between the means as large as those we observed. However, Gosset realized that the difference between the means depends on the scale that is used to measure the variables (for instance, measuring in millimeters results in a numerical difference that is ten times greater than measuring in centimeters). A different set of DIFs expected under the null hypothesis would therefore have to be calculated for each scale of measurement, or when we change from comparing smaller things, such as mice to comparing larger things, such as men.

To remove the problem of scale of measurement, Gosset standardized the differences by dividing by the standard deviation to put all of the results on a common scale (see Chapter 3 if you have forgotten what a standard deviation is). His new formula became DIF/S_{DIF}. Do not worry about S_{DIF} at this moment, it is only necessary for you to realize that this was a mathematical trick to get rid of the scale problem. Gosset's DIF/S_{DIF} was later called the "t" statistic (see Mosteller and Tukey 1968 for other important historical implications of Gosset's test).

However, life was not easy at the beginning of the 20th century. Remember that we used a computer to calculate 100 DIFs because the process of flipping a coin and calculating a new DIF for each null-hypothesis sample can be extremely time-consuming. Gosset did not have access to a high-speed computer, and he simulated the process by writing 3000 numbers on pieces of cardboard, shuffling them and then taking 750 samples of four (Student 1908). This was adequate to illustrate the general distribution of his statistic. However, he found that the graph was not very satisfactory because he rounded off the numbers when he wrote them on the pieces of cardboard.

Gosset wasn't about to write out another 3000 numbers, and he realized that physically taking samples was too complicated to be used in most situations. Therefore, he embarked on a "what if" exercise that only a mathematician could envisage. He used the following logic: If we know something about the distribution of measurements in our hypothetical null population, and the distribution of these measurements has a form that mathematical theory can work with, we can work out what the distribution of the t-statistic should be when the null hypothesis is correct. He used the data collected to estimate some characteristics of the hypothetical null population.

> **Population characteristics are called parameters.**

Hence, this type of test is called a parametric test.

As he did not have the technology to generate lots of values of t, he used mathematical theory to estimate the proportion of the hypothetical ts that would be as large as, or larger than, the observed t. Gosset's brilliance as a mathematician is demonstrated by the fact that, when his assumptions about the distribution of the hypothetical population are correct, his method gives almost exactly the same result as our computer-based method.

How Statisticians Count Independent Observations

When the null hypothesis is correct, a different population of t exists for every combination of number of observations in each sample. Earlier, we compared five streams with fish to five streams without fish. However, had we used seven streams with fish and five streams without fish, we would have had different populations of DIF and t. This does not matter much for our computer-based method. The difference in time taken to calculate DIF for samples of five or samples of seven is less than a millisecond. However, at the turn of the century, statisticians could not calculate all of the possible results by hand. They therefore invented the concept of critical values for statistics.

Although they could not present the probability associated with every value of t when the null hypothesis was correct, they could work out some critical values. They could say, "If you had five observations in the first sample, and seven in the second, all values of t greater than 1.81 have less than a 10% chance of being observed when the null hypothesis is correct. Values of t greater than 2.95 have less than 1% chance of being observed." These critical values were used to construct tables of critical values like those found at the backs of most statistical texts.

Most modern computer programs give exact probabilities of the null hypothesis being true and statistical tables are rarely used anymore. This example does, however, introduce the concept of degrees of freedom used in statistical tests. To work out the probability associated with any particular value of a statistic, we need to know how many independent observations were used to calculate it. Degrees of freedom for statistical tests are usually said to be the number of independent observations less the number of parameters estimated. In our example, we had 10 rivers, and we had to estimate a mean and a standard deviation to construct the distribution of results expected when the null hypothesis is correct. The degrees of freedom for the t-statistic in our example are therefore $10 - 2 = 8$. However, to correctly interpret statistical tables, we really need two numbers: the number of parameters estimated, and the number of independent observations. It would be more consistent with other more complex tests if we considered the degrees of freedom for the t-test we carried out to be 1 and 8. We do not have to present the first number because t-tests always estimate only two parameters.

You do not have to worry about this now, but do note that the degrees of freedom are associated with the number of independent observations. If your observations are not independent (i.e., you committed pseudoreplication), you enter the table at the wrong point, and the probabilities you calculate are pseudoprobabilities that cannot be related to any practical null hypothesis.

Unfortunately most of the probabilities in the literature are pseudoprobabilities that do little more than indicate that the author belongs to the world of science. They transmit no objective information about the outside world.

Do not worry if you found the last section hard to understand. It is only important that you understand that statisticians such as Gosset followed the same process that we did in our coin-tossing test.

Step 1. He visualized the expected result when the hypothesis he was testing was correct.

Step 2. He visualized the expected result when the hypothesis he was testing was not correct.

Step 3. He created a measurement that reflected the difference expected between the results in Step 1 and Step 2. This measurement is now called the "t" statistic.

Step 4. He used mathematical theory to obtain many values of the statistic using a process in which the null hypothesis was true (i.e., when his hypothesis was wrong).

Step 5. He used mathematics to compare the value of the statistic for the observed data with the values of the statistic obtained when the null hypothesis was true (null values). Then, he used the proportion of the null values equal to or greater than the observed value as an indication of the probability of obtaining the observed value when the null hypothesis was true.

Step 6. He made a decision as to whether that probability was so small that he could reject the null hypothesis, and continue to believe in his hypothesis.

Understanding the Statistical World with Ease

If you have read some statistics texts and remember something about normal and other types of distributions you may like to read the following section.

However, please forget it immediately afterwards because the world becomes unnecessarily complex when we get away from our simple dispersion graphs.

One reason that students become confused about distributions of statistics or data values is that the distribution of values of a measurement or a statistic are always given on the horizontal axis in statistics books. Therefore, it is necessary to invert the graphs.

Figure 5.4

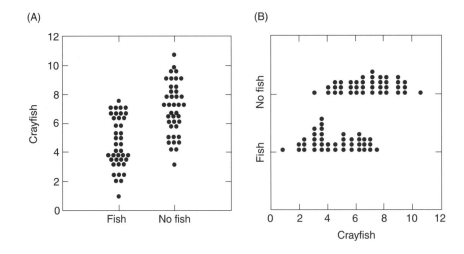

Consider the distribution of the data points in Figure 5.4A. We related the values of crayfish to the categories of stream. Because we believe that the densities of crayfish depend on the categories of stream, and not vice versa, we put the densities of crayfish on the vertical (y) axis, following the convention that the dependent variable goes on the y-axis. However, had we had only one category of stream, as in parametric null hypotheses, the only thing that could vary would be the frequency of data values for each value of crayfish density. Therefore, distributions are conventionally given by putting what used to be the dependent variable on the horizontal (x) axis. Figure 5.4A becomes Figure 5.4B.

However, the mathematics does not see the individual points and, assuming that a particular distribution called the "normal," uses the data to estimate the

Figure 5.5

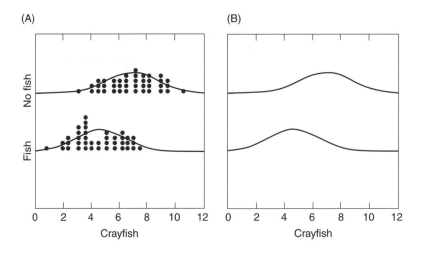

characteristics of this distribution (Figure 5.5A), we then can discard the data (Figure 5.5B).

We can see that the normal distribution does not seem to be a very good approximation to the data from streams with fish, but this does not generally affect the validity of the commonly used statistical tests. The distribution of data expected when the null hypothesis is true is in fact a single hybrid curve that is a sort of mathematical average of the two curves in Figure 5.5B. We use this curve to estimate the difference in the means for samples of given sizes when the null hypothesis is correct.

The sort of distribution expected is similar to that of our DIF (see Figure 5.3). To compare our observed value of DIF to the distribution of DIFs expected when the null hypothesis is true (Figure 5.6A, which is the same as Figure 5.3), we could invert the axes, rub out the points, and just compare the position of the black dot along the *x*-axis with the theoretical distribution of DIF (Figure 5.6B).

This is what most textbooks would have us do. However, it usually does not aid comprehension. Mathematicians do not physically sample their null populations, but it helps if you always consider that they have, and try to imagine distributions of statistics on a vertical scale as though you had physically measured them. Almost all of the analyses we will consider are mainly concerned with vertical variation in values on our graphs. Therefore, it only complicates things if we keep switching graph orientation.

All this is getting a bit complicated so we had better get back to some real-life examples. In the next chapter, we will consider how you can efficiently test for any difference among a multitude of categories.

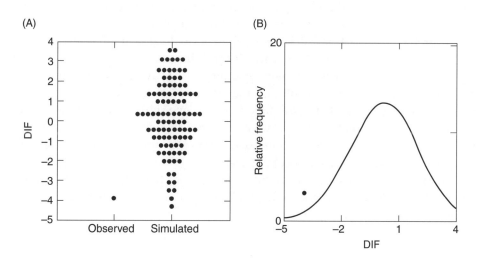

Figure 5.6

## CHAPTER 6

"Improbable things do occur."

How to Avoid Accumulating Risk in Simple Comparisons

What Sort of Risk Are We Worried About?

First of all, we had better be clear about what sort of risk we are concerned with. We reject the null hypothesis when we obtain a result that would be very unlikely if the null hypothesis were true. However, this does not mean that the result could never occur if the null hypothesis were true. There is always the risk of rejecting the null hypothesis when it is correct, even if our calculated probability is very low. We deal with probabilities, and improbable things do occur. The probability of you being killed in your car on the way home from work is very low. In fact, it is so low that you probably do not even think about it. However, hundreds of people will die in their cars on their way home tonight.

The probabilities that statisticians usually work with are very different from the probabilities we worry about in normal life and this can lead to problems. This is especially true because scientists have generally tried to avoid deciding that a phenomenon exists when it does not. This makes sense because science advances on previous knowledge. If that knowledge is faulty, everything that follows will be wrong. If we decide that predatory fish affect crayfish densities when they do not, we will stop looking for the real cause of changes in crayfish densities, and probably invest in inappropriate remedial measures.

Traditionally, scientists are only willing to consider the existence of a phenomenon if there is less than a one in 20 (0.05) chance that it does not exist. They do not jump to conclusions easily.

Falsely rejecting the null hypothesis and deciding that a phenomenon exists when it does not is called a Type I error, and conventional statistics guards against our making this type of error.

However, Type I errors are not always the most costly. This is easily seen with a personal example. Imagine that you have fallen in love with a statistician, who has just returned from a statistical conference where he or she indulged in illicit activities for which statisticians are not famous. Your prospective spouse says, "Don't worry, I have conducted the appropriate tests, and the chances that I have not contracted a dangerous sexually transmitted disease is 6%, and a probability of 0.06 is not sufficient to reject the null hypothesis that I am not contagious."

This is a perfectly valid statistical and scientific conclusion. However, making a Type I error is probably the least of your worries. In this case, the probability of accepting the null hypothesis when it is false is the most costly alternative. This is called a Type II error. Even an 80% chance that your partner is not carrying a potentially fatal, contagious disease is probably not sufficient for you to dispense with new tests and continue with the relationship.

The probability of making a Type II error is generally inversely proportional to the probability of making a Type I error.

Therefore, many scientists use probabilities much greater than 0.05 when a Type II error involves a high cost. This commonly occurs in studies dealing with human health, the extinction of species, and when the premature rejection of a hypothesis leads to the abandonment of a potentially important line of research. Very few scientists accept an arbitrary significance level of 0.05 to plan their personal lives. It reflects on the seriousness with which they consider their science that many of them are willing to accept it in their professional activities.

The probability that you decide a priori is sufficient to reject the null hypothesis (conventionally, but not always 0.05) is called the critical level, or "α." The probability of not rejecting the null hypothesis when it is false (i.e., committing a Type II error) is called β by statisticians, and the capacity of a test to reject the null hypothesis when it is indeed false is called the "power of the test." There is no absolute measure of power, so it is usually expressed as a comparison with the most powerful test available.

We do not have time to belabor the importance of Type II errors and for most of the following discussion we assume, as do most textbooks, that we are dealing with situations in which a Type I error would be the most costly. This assumption will facilitate your learning of the general concepts. However, we hope that you will not forget about Type II errors in your applied research, and that you will evaluate the likelihood of these types of errors (useful references include Koele [1982], Huberty [1987], and Green [1989]).

Given some preliminary data, there are computer programs that can calculate the sample size necessary to detect a specified size of effect at a specified probability (e.g., SIMSTAT, Péladeau 1966). However, there are some tricky mathematics involved, and you will generally do better if you make sure that you have convincing hypothetical graphs.

Using Variability to Recognize a Difference

In the previous chapter, we considered an example in which we compared one sample to another, and by constructing a null hypothesis, evaluated the probability of falsely declaring that something other than chance caused the differences between them. It does not matter whether you use physical permutation (our DIF test) or complicated mathematics (such as Student's *t*-test) to generate the results expected when the null hypothesis is correct, the principles are the same. However, our null hypothesis related only to a comparison between two groups. We now consider what happens when we compare more than two groups. Perhaps our biologist was interested in crayfish densities in streams without fish (SWOF), streams with carnivorous fish (SWCF), and streams with herbivorous fish (SWHF) (Figure 6.1).

Figure 6.1

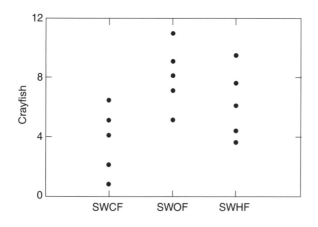

We could use our coin-tossing test or Student's *t*-test to compare SWOF to SWCF, SWOF to SWHF, and SWCF to SWHF. However, each time we carry out a test we risk making a mistake. For now, we will follow convention and assume that the null hypothesis (no difference between samples) should only be rejected if it has a one in 20 chance, or less, of being correct. If nothing other than the vagaries of sampling caused the differences in means among the samples, we only reject the null hypothesis when 5% or less of the simulated DIFs (or calculated ts) are less than the DIF (or t) for the observed data. Therefore, the chance of committing a Type I error when we compare SWOF to SWCF is about one in 20. However, if we then compare SWOF to SWHF, there is also a one in twenty risk of finding a difference when it does not exist. The overall probability of finding a difference that does not exist is now about two in 20. With three tests, it is about three in 20, and keeps increasing, though not linearly, with the number of tests.

This cumulative error rate is familiar to us in our everyday lives, though when we are young, we tend to think that it cannot happen to us. Most parents of adolescent children have felt the dread when their child borrows the car and drives too fast, or partakes of dangerous sports such as mountain climbing. Every time the child survives a dangerous activity they become more convinced that they are immune to the dangers. However, the parent knows that if the behavior is repeated often enough, a small chance of death becomes almost a certainty. Scientists also tend to shrug off the problem of repeated tests because they are sure that their hypotheses are correct. It usually takes a few nasty experiences to convince them that the laws of probability apply to everyone. Tukey (1991) gives an illuminating discussion of cumulative risk-taking in relation to everyday activities that have nothing to do with scientific experimentation.

Long ago, Bonferroni suggested that when we test a hypothesis a number of times, we can correct the probability of rejecting the overall null hypothesis of no difference among the samples by multiplying the probability for each test by the number of tests. If any of the modified probabilities are low enough to reject the null hypothesis, then the overall null hypothesis is rejected at that level of probability. In our case, we decided to reject the null hypothesis only if there was a one in 20 chance, or less, of it being correct. Therefore, if any of the probabilities calculated from the tests are less than 0.05 after being multiplied by three, we reject the null hypothesis.

The Bonferroni correction is simple, easy to perform, and about as good as any other test when just a few tests have been made. However, when there are many tests, the Bonferroni procedure tends to accept the null hypothesis more than it should (Type II error). Modifications of this procedure can increase its power (Rice 1989, Benjamini and Hochberg 1995). Note that the method advocated by Benjamini and Hochberg (1995) also changes the question.

Ronald Fisher developed a better method for comparing many categories. The problem with using DIF or t is that a single graph such as Figure 5.9 has many DIFs or ts. Fisher reasoned that it would be more efficient if the graph could yield just one statistic that reflected the overall difference among categories. Fisher was a mathematician and he could think in terms of squared differences; (see Chapter 3 if you think that you need to know more about squared differences—you probably don't). However, we will consider the concept using only the amplitude, which you can

Figure 6.2

(A) Observed data

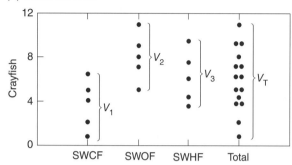

(B) Null hypothesis

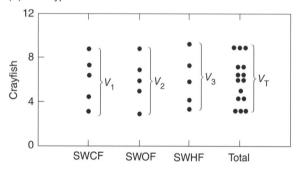

easily recognize on a graph (Figure 6.2).

We have included another category, Total, for the data from all types of rivers combined. If the variability within each category is the same, and the means differ, then the total variability will be much greater than the variability within any one category. We used the range to represent the variability (V), and a test of this form can be carried out using the range (Beyer 1968, page 385). However, the same logic applies to any measure of the variability (Fisher used a measure called the variance). In mathematical terms, when the null hypothesis is not true, as in Figure 6.2A, this relationship can be represented by the following equation:

$$V_1 = V_2 = V_3 < V_T$$

This can also be written as:

$$\text{Mean } V_i < V_T$$

> **If equations give you the chills, just make sure that you can interpret the graph.**

Figure 6.2B shows a result expected when the null hypothesis is correct. There is no difference between the means, and in this case we can see that the total variability is the same as the variability within each category. We can say this mathematically in the following equation:

$$V_1 = V_2 = V_3 = V_T$$

We can write that the Mean $V_i = V_T$. Hopefully, you can see this on the graph, though of course the graph for this example (see Figure 6.2B) is a little contrived. The variability in each category is almost the same, and the means of the result expected when the null hypothesis is true are exactly the same in our graph. Obviously, chance does not allow this to happen with real samples. However, we do not expect differences greater than those caused by chance when the null hypothesis is true.

Comparison of the two graphs shows that when the null hypothesis is true, we expect the mean variation within categories to be about the same as the total variation. A simple statistic that reflects this is the total variation divided by the mean variation within categories (i.e., V_T/V_i). We call our conceptual statistic VR, the variation ratio. When the null hypothesis is correct, Mean $V_T = V_i$ and $VR = 1$. When the null hypothesis is incorrect, $V_T > V_i$ and $VR > 1$. Just as Student did not use the simple statistic DIF, Fisher did not use VR. He used the ratio of two variances (if you really need to know what a variance is, consult Chapter 3). Fisher called his statistic the variance ratio, but in his honor it has been named the F-statistic. Fisher's F is constructed a little differently from VR, as we will show in the section on partitioning variability, but its expected value when the null hypothesis is true is still 1. If the equations are too much for you, return to Figure 6.2 to make sure that you can see the difference between the situation when the null hypothesis is not correct (see Figure 6.2A), and when it is correct (see Figure 6.2B).

> **The equations and statistics just reflect the difference seen on the graph.**

To generate samples of F when the null hypothesis was true, Fisher had to resort to some pretty serious mathematics. Like Student, he assumed a normal distribution of values in the hypothetical null population, though the results of his test are not very sensitive to moderate deviations from that assumption. If you are worried that the form of the population from which your samples were collected is not normal, then you can use a permutation test like the one we used for DIF. Manly (1997) gives many examples of permutation tests that do not have all the assumptions of parametric tests.

An Important Assumption

The logic of Fisher's and Student's tests are quite similar. In fact, for comparisons between two samples, $F = t^2$. However, there is one assumption of both tests that cannot easily be ignored. Both F and t are sensitive to differences between means, and to differences in the variation within categories. Unexpectedly large values of F indicate that either the means are different, or that the variability within categories is different.

> **If you want to test for a difference between means you have to assume that the variability within categories is the same.**

Figure 6.3

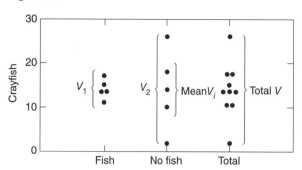

Both F and t are calculated by dividing the variability among the means by the mean variability within categories. The logic is that if the samples were taken from a single population with that mean variability (the null hypothesis), you would only expect the observed differences among the means at the probability given in the table or computer. However, Figure 6.3 shows an example in which the variability differs among levels.

The computer does not "see" the individual variability, but creates the null distribution based on the mean V_i. It would be much easier to encounter an extreme value for a mean of a sample taken from the distribution represented by the no-fish category than from the distribution represented by the mean V_i. Therefore, the null distribution is not correct, and the probabilities tend to be too small. If we apply Fisher's test (called analysis of variance, or ANOVA for short), we would likely discover an apparently significant difference among the means, but the difference would be due to underestimating the variability in the null hypothesis. If we had a hypothesis about the means, this would lead us to commit a Type I error; in other words, we reject the null hypothesis when it is true.

Although most textbooks are concerned with equality of variances, Fisher's test may be more sensitive to departures from symmetry. Analysis of variance, and many of its randomization analogues, is very sensitive to extreme values, referred to as outliers (Manly 1997), so it is important to inspect graphs before applying any of the statistical evaluations.

A purely statistical abuse of Type II errors is commonly found in tests to determine whether the assumptions of an analysis have been met. Levene's test checks the assumption that the variances within levels are not sufficiently different to cause improbable values of the F-statistic. The use of low critical values of P is generally considered "safe" or "conservative." However, for tests of assumptions, a Type I error is not the most costly. If you wrongly fail to determine that the assumption is incorrect, you will attribute a significant effect where none exists. Authors often recommend a critical value of $P = 0.05$ for such tests (e.g., Dytham 1999). If the calculated probability is 0.07, this is equivalent to writing "there is about a 7% chance that my conclusion is not gibberish." Does this seem "safe" to you?

> **For some reason, biologists have a fixation on comparing means. However, very often changes in variability are just as important (see, e.g., Callaghan & Holloway 1999, Benedetti-Cecchi 2003).**

From here on we concentrate on variability, though sometimes we use variability to make inferences about means or other characteristics (parameters) of populations.

The analysis of variance tells us that there is a difference among the means. However, it does not tell us which means are different. To determine this you have to look at the graph or use a weaker test to try to locate the difference (e.g., Day and Quinn 1989). We will not deal with those tests here, since if you understand the concepts behind multiple testing and ANOVA, you will be able to understand the comparisons of treatments after an ANOVA.

Before we leave Fisher's analysis of variance model, we should consider some terminology that will be useful when we treat more complicated examples. We return to the data in Figure 6.1, in which the variability within categories is similar, but for simplicity we consider only two categories: streams with fish and streams without fish (Figure 6.4).

Partitioning Variance

We now have the variability within categories ($V_i = V_1 = V_2$), the variability between means of categories (V_{Fish}), and the total variability (V_T). Conceptually, we say that the difference between the means is due to the presence of fish (this is usually called a treatment or factor effect [V_{Factor}]). The difference between the total variability and V_{Fish} is due to residual variability that cannot be attributed to any particular cause. Residual variability is sometimes called error variability, but this implies that variability is not a natural part of the real world, and the terminology is not helpful.

An analogous process using the variance instead of the amplitude is called partitioning variance. The calculations are a little more complicated but the principle is the same. It is this process that is used in most of the more complicated analyses we will consider in the rest of this book. Therefore, if you have trouble seeing the partitions on the graphs, please

Figure 6.4

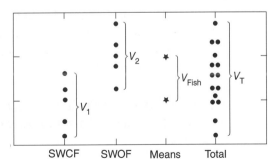

Figure 6.5

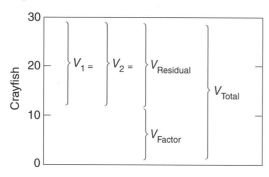

review this chapter. We will continually refer to partitioning such as seen in Figure 6.4, and you must be able to visualize this in terms of data points. You should be able to visualize the following simple equation in Figures 6.4 and 6.5:

$$V_{Factor} + V_{Residual} = V_{Total}$$

Figure 6.5 is basically the same as Figure 6.4. However, in order to make it clearer in relation to the general concept of variance partitioning, we modified it slightly. To illustrate residual variation, we removed the data points and aligned V_1 and V_2. In Figure 6.4, the variability due to the presence of fish is presented as V_{Fish}; in Figure 6.5 it is presented as V_{Factor}.

Fisher worked with sums of squares (SS) and made decisions based on mean squares (MS), but you do not have to know how to calculate these to understand their principles. Rather than compare the residual variation to the total variation, Fisher's F is the ratio of the factor (treatment) mean square to the residual mean square. The factor mean square, as calculated in ANOVA, does not only represent the variability among the means. It estimates the variability among means plus the variability within levels (residual).

Mean squares are sums of squares divided by degrees of freedom (df). Thus, they are analogous to the variances we calculated in Chapter 3. However, most are compound variances. The mean square of the factor is an estimate of the variance due to the factor plus the variance in the residual ($\delta^2_{Factor} + \delta^2_{Residual}$), and the mean square of the residual is another estimate of the variance in the residual ($\delta^2_{Residual}$). Conceptually, and forgetting a few constants, we have the following equation:

$$F = (\delta^2_{Factor} + \delta^2_{Residual})/(\delta^2_{Residual})$$

When the variance due to the factor is zero (the null hypothesis is correct), the right-hand side of the equation reduces to ($\delta^2_{Residual} / \delta^2_{Residual}$) and $F = 1$. Because they are based on compound variances, F-ratios can get complicated, as we will see in Chapter 8.

However, the concept that variability can uniquely be partitioned into a portion that relates to the factor and a portion that relates to the residual, is simple.

Students often ask how ANOVA programs can calculate $F < 1$, if the previous equation is correct. This happens because of the vagaries of sampling, and because a statistician's "expected value" is different from the value we expect to find. In fact, most F's are less than 1 when the null hypothesis is correct. The expected value for a statistician is the value you would expect if you repeated the exercise a great number of times and took the average. For a right skewed distribution, such as that of F, which can have very large positive values but not negative values, an occasional very large value can keep the mean at one, even though most of the values are less than one.

Unbiased expected values for statisticians relate to the mean value expected over an infinite number of trials. An ecologist is usually trying to make a decision based on a single experiment. F-tables take into account the skewed distribution of F, and give the correct probabilities. However, if you are constructing your own tests, make sure that you understand that "expected" values may not be close to the ones you will frequently find. Caughley and Sinclair (1994, page 210) give an example for the Petersen estimate of population size, which shows that the expected value of this statistic is much larger than the great majority of values calculated.

Many statistics courses start with examples of contingency tables as the simplest way to analyze categories. However, such analyses are only simple in the classroom and are virtually useless for ecological studies (see Chapter 4, Hurlbert 1984, or Magnusson 1999). Usually, if it is necessary to deal with categories, analysis of variance is simpler and more efficient than analyses based on contingency tables. In the next chapter, we will deal with analyses that are even more general than analysis of variance of categorical factors.

## CHAPTER 7

"Scientific study usually starts with categorization, but tends to stagnate until someone starts to study process rather than just pattern."

Analyses for a World with All Shades of Gray

What Sort of Risk Are We Worried About?

So far, we've spent a lot of time considering how to test for differences between categories. In our everyday lives we are suspicious of people who like to put things in categories. We call such people sexists, racists, xenophobes, and other derogatory names. Usually, they are not very socially competent people. As with social interactions, a scientific study usually starts with categorization, but tends to stagnate until someone starts to study the process rather than just the pattern.

To understand color you have to understand that the human eye creates the astounding diversity of named colors from mixtures of just three different types of color receptors in the retina. Technicians used this information to make color printers that generate astoundingly beautiful reproductions using only red, green, blue, and black dots. However, in the final analysis, the only thing that changes between one color and another is the electromagnetic wave length, a continuous variable.

In our everyday lives, we recognize "fixed" sexual differences, but this gross categorization is of diminishing value to medicine. Most drugs do not interact with "sex," they interact with hormone level, fat content of the body, metabolic rate, bone density, and a multitude of factors that are only loosely associated with external genital appearance. Even socially, the categories do not always work well. We will discuss some of the reasons why in the next chapter, but first we need to understand how categories can distort the way we see the world. If categories do not work well in social relationships, why do they have such an exalted position in science?

Putting the World into Boxes

First, we will consider what happens when we categorize a continuous phenomenon, and then we will investigate more direct methods of attacking this problem. Figure 7.1 shows some data on the activity of an insect in relation to air temperature. Both John and Mary decide to sample low (= 1) and high (= 2) levels of temperature, but they use different levels to represent "high" and "low" (Figures 7.1A and 7.1B). They have no knowledge of the data that can be collected outside of their categories, and they each produce a graph to show their results (Figure 7.2).

As they have read the previous chapter of this text, they decide that they will test to see whether differences between the means of the "high" and "low" samples are due to the vagaries of sampling. They could use our DIF test, but they decide to use Student's t-test with a correction for the differences between the variances within categories. You do not have to worry about this shortcut they used to get around one of the assumptions of the t-test; the test still gives a result similar to the DIF test.

John's test estimates a probability of 0.78 that the null hypothesis is correct, so he rejects his hypothesis that temperature affects the activity of the insect. Mary's test estimates a probability of 0.035 that the null hypothesis is correct, so she rejects the null hypothesis as improbable, and continues to accept her hypothesis

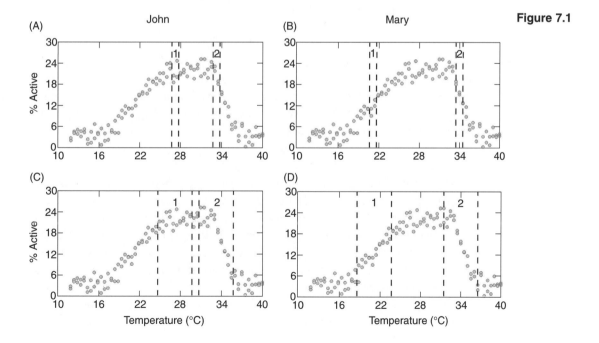

Figure 7.1

Figure 7.2

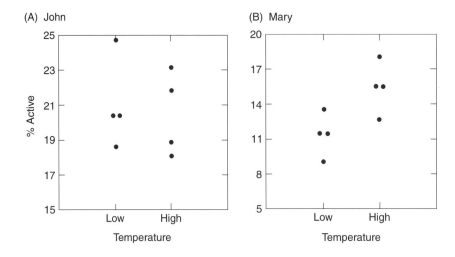

(A) John   (B) Mary

% Active

Low   High
Temperature

Low   High
Temperature

that temperature affects the activity of the insect. However, we did not have to use any fancy statistics or Popperian logic; most people will come to the same conclusions simply by looking at Figure 7.2.

Getting contradictory results is understandable in terms of our analysis of variance model. We said that all of the variability due to sampling is in the residual variability. Our conceptual model is as follows:

$$V_{\text{Residual}} + V_{\text{Factor}} = V_{\text{Total}}$$

However, there is another source of variation that affects the total, and that is variation due to sampling only some of the levels of the factor. Therefore, our conceptual model should contain a term for variability due to sampling only some of the possible levels of the factor. We denote this term as V_{Levels}. The conceptual model therefore becomes as follows:

$$V_{\text{Residual}} + V_{\text{Factor}} + V_{\text{Levels}} = V_{\text{Total}}$$

When we sample all levels of a factor, it is said to be "fixed." If we sample only a small proportion of the levels of the factor, it is called a "random" factor. However, neither of these terms is very appropriate. Rarely are the levels of a random factor randomly sampled from all possible levels, and the sampling design can greatly affect the outcome. We are not going to discuss this any further because when we categorize a continuous variable, there are other illogical effects that make interpretation even more difficult.

Returning to the lower part of Figure 7.1, we see that in an alternative experimental design, John and Mary used exactly the same mean levels of temperature

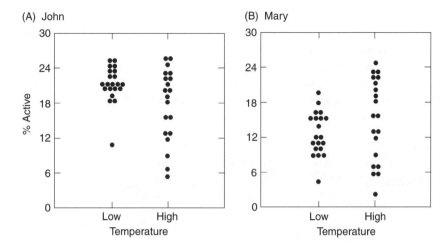

Figure 7.3

for "high" and "low" as before, but have used wider intervals for their categories. If we create graphs of their results exactly as we did for the narrow intervals, the conclusions are reversed (Figure 7.3).

Using the same statistical test, John now rejects the null hypothesis as improbable ($P = 0.013$), and Mary accepts the null hypothesis ($P = 0.22$). Table 7.1 compares John's and Mary's conclusions when they use narrow and wide intervals to define their categories.

Our conceptual model now indicates that the total variation not only depends on the levels sampled, but also on the width of the intervals chosen to represent a category:

$$V_{\text{Residual}} + V_{\text{Factor}} + V_{\text{Levels}} + V_{\text{Width}} = V_{\text{Total}}$$

There are some statistical techniques to deal with the variation due to V_{Levels} and we will consider them in the Chapter 8. However, there is no objective method of dealing with V_{Width}.

By now, we hope that you are questioning why researchers bother to categorize continuous variables. One part of the answer is that we feel more comfortable with apparently simple categories. The other reason is that when we have more than one factor, "strong inference" experiments are usually only possible when we use categories. If there are an infinite number of levels, it is impossible to ensure that all levels of each factor are measured under all levels of the other factors (Magnusson 2002a).

Table 7.1		
Interval	**John**	**Mary**
Wide	Significant	Not significant
Narrow	Not significant	Significant

There may be a great deal of information in the natural order of the categories that standard analysis of variance of categorical variables cannot pick up (Gaines and Rice 1990). Basically, when a researcher categorizes a continuous variable in the name of experimental design, weak inference about a strong category (there is only one) is being traded for strong inference about subjective categories. This is related to our discussions of scale in previous chapters. Only hierarchies based on scale (measurable quantities) can have an objective basis.

> **Hierarchies based on "levels" are always subjective and can impede the advancement of science (Allen 1998).**

Describing a Straight World

To understand how computers and statistical tests deal with continuous variables, we need to start with the simplest sort of relationship, a straight line. Figure 7.4 shows a map of the trees in six reserves.

Our model of this system is very simple. We expect that there will be a direct relationship between the reserve area and the number of trees in each reserve if the distribution of trees is random with respect to reserves. The model is represented by the line in Figure 7.5. The points represent the number of trees actually counted in each reserve.

Our theoretical model is pretty good, judging by the fact that most of the points are close to the line. The theoretical model can be represented by an equation of the following form:

$$\text{Number of plants} = A + B \times \text{Reserve size}$$

Textbooks would use Greek letters for A and B as they are theoretical and not estimated from the data. For our example, $A = 0$ and $B = 1$. Substituting in the equation you can see that this just says that when there is no reserve (reserve size = 0) there are no trees. It also says that for every extra hectare of size, the number of trees increases by one individual on average.

This general equation can be used to describe any straight line. The A is the elevation, or the value of the dependent variable, when the independent variable is equal to zero. The B term is the slope, or the amount that the dependent variable increases for a one-unit increase in the independent variable. As most of the

Figure 7.4

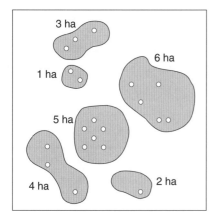

common analyses are based on variants of this equation, it is worthwhile to spend some time making sure that you can visualize the equation on the graph.

However, most of the time we are not dealing with theoretical equations, and we try to determine the position of the line from the observed data. Figure 7.6 shows such a relationship between insect activity and temperature in the range between 26° and 36° C. We do not know the true relationship between insect activity and temperature. We put a line on the graph that represents what we think the relationship is likely to be based on the distribution of points.

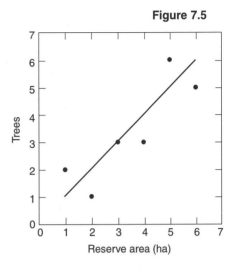

Figure 7.5

When we, other people, or computer programs, put straight lines on graphs, we use some method of minimizing the average distance of the points from the line.

This seems straightforward, but there are in fact many different distances that can be minimized. Figure 7.7 shows a portion of our graph and three distances that might be minimized.

Figure 7.7A shows a logical distance to minimize for two of the points. Minimizing the distance of the points from any part of the line as shown in Figure 7.7A is called "major axis regression." Finding the position of the line which results in the minimum area of the triangles formed by horizontal and vertical lines from the points to the line is "reduced major axis regression" (Figure 7.7B). Both of these methods are logical and similar to what most people would say they are doing. Minimizing only the vertical distance from the points to the line does not appear very logical (Figure 7.7C).

Minimizing the sum of the squared vertical distances from the line (see Figure 7.7C, shaded areas) seems even more illogical. It is, however, what the most common statistical methods do. All methods have advantages and drawbacks. For a discussion

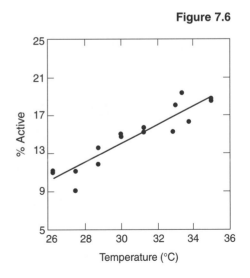

Figure 7.6

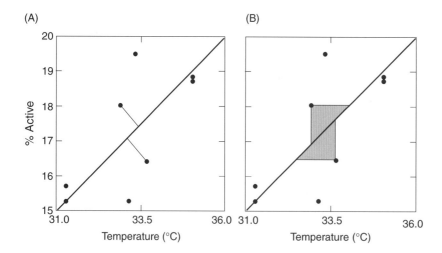

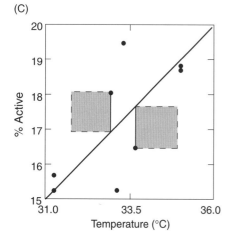

(A)

(B)

Figure 7.7

(C)

of some of these issues the reader should consult Ricker (1973).

Minimizing only the squared vertical distances from the line allows a wider range of more complicated analyses and is generally the most useful for prediction. For obvious reasons (see Figure 7.7C), it is called "least-squares regression" and is logically and mathematically equivalent to Fisher's analysis of variance for categorical independent variables. Major variants of most of the common analyses only consist of minimizing different distances. We will consider some of these in Chapter 11. These distances are residuals, as is the variation within categories in analysis of variance of categories.

How Good a Fit Is the Model?

The variation about the line is the residual variation not explained by our model (the line); Figure 7.8 illustrates this. The proportion of the variability attributable to the independent variable (in this case temperature), when variability is measured by the sum of squares (see Chapter 3) is called the coefficient of determination and is abbreviated as r^2 (or R^2 if there is more than one independent variable; see Chapter 8). Although you almost certainly cannot visualize sums of squares (imagine the sum of the shaded areas in Figure 7.7C), make sure that you can visualize the sort of variation it represents in Figure 7.8 as the $V_{\text{Factor}}/V_{\text{Total}}$. When performing analyses involving categories, we have to assume that the variation within categories is constant. When performing regressions, we need to assume that the variation around the line is constant. Although r^2 is one of the most used statistics, it is not a good measure of the magnitude of the effect in categorical analysis (Rosenthal and Rubin 1982).

When we estimate the position of the line, we use lowercase letters to represent the elevation and inclination in the descriptive equation $Y = a + b \times X$, where Y is any dependent variable (in our case, % active), and X is any independent variable (in our case "temperature"). The letters a and b represent estimates of parameters (statistics) because they

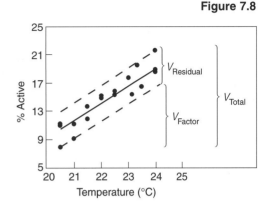

Figure 7.8

describe the population of points on which the regression was based. The null hypothesis could be represented by the situation in Figure 7.9.

As with the analysis of categories, when the variation in the residual is as great as the total variation we assume that there is no effect of the variable that we measured, or $V_{Factor} = 0$.

> In fact, the analysis of variance model is completely general and most computer programs treat analysis of variance of categorical data and regression in exactly the same way.

Therefore, for regression, as for analysis of variance, our conceptual models start off as the following simple equation:

$$V_{Factor} + V_{Residual} = V_{Total}$$

We do not have to worry about selection of categories because we have only one category. However, we do have to worry about the width of the category. If the relationship really is linear, the probability of detecting a relationship increases as we increase the width of the interval. Figure 7.10 shows how the strong relationship in Figure 7.8 disappears if we cut the range of temperature in half. It is obvious that what we have done is decreased the variation due to the factor while maintaining the variation in the residual.

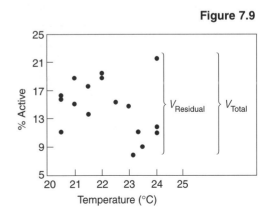

Figure 7.9

Figure 7.10

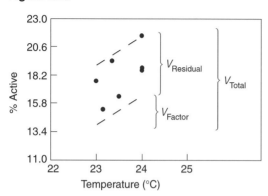

Therefore, our conceptual model must consider variability because of the width of the interval, even when the relationship is linear:

$$V_{\text{Residual}} + V_{\text{Factor}} + V_{\text{Width}} = V_{\text{Total}}$$

Fortunately, if the relationship is linear, increasing the interval can only increase our chances of detecting an effect. Increasing the interval can only decrease the chance of detecting an effect when nonlinear continuous variables are categorized as they were in the first example given in this chapter.

It is important not to get lost in the details. All we have done in this chapter is apply the analysis of variance model for categorical data to linear relationships and observed that the concept is general. We learned that linear relationships are described by two parameters, the elevation (*a*) and the slope (*b*), and that if we estimated them correctly, the underlying relationship is described by equations of the following form:

$$Y = a + b \times X + e$$

The *e* just indicates that any observed *Y* will deviate from the line by some amount which is attributable to the effect of random or unstudied processes. Few people have trouble with these simple mathematics, but if you do, review this chapter before proceeding to Chapter 8.

The ability to interpret statistics is not as important as the ability to interpret graphs.

See Anscombe (1973) for an example of five graphs that have exactly the same statistical summaries, but totally different biological interpretations. There are methods of linearizing nonlinear relationships by transforming variables, and we can obtain more "correct" models by minimizing residuals that are not squared vertical distances (see Chapter 11). Also, it is often more realistic to calculate regression lines that represent the limits to effects rather than the mean effect (Cade et al. 1999). However, you will get a better conceptual understanding if you proceed directly to the next chapter.

## CHAPTER 8

"Univariate tests are usually redundant."

Real-World Problems: More Than One Factor

Although the examples of statistical tests given in the previous chapters were useful to illustrate principles, it is important to realize that those univariate (one-independent variable) tests are usually redundant. They can be replaced by simple dispersion graphs, which can be represented by flow charts such as that shown in Figure 8.1. Inexperienced researchers can be fooled by graphical illusions (see Ellison 1993), but novices are far more likely to be fooled by statistical illusions (Anscombe 1973). If the statistical analysis suggests a conclusion different from the pattern you can see on the graph, do not trust either. Many statistical treatments are trivial and serve no objective purpose other than cultural identification (Yoccoz 1991, Cherry 1999, Johnson 1999).

If the independent variable is categorical and has more than two levels, the arrow can only represent the flow of influence, it cannot indicate what sort of effect the variable will have. For instance, if "trees" represent "species of trees," we can imagine that increasing some species will be good for monkeys, others could be bad, and monkeys may be indifferent to many.

We also have the same problem if the relationship is continuous but not linear, or at least monotonic (i.e., it either exclusively increases or decreases). An increase in a continuous variable, such as tree density, may cause monkey numbers to increase when trees are sparse, but a similar increase may decrease monkey numbers when trees become dense. Figure 2.6 illustrates this type of relationship between insect activity and temperature; it is very common in biology. We start with a much simpler model, which is uncommon in nature, but very common in statistical models. We assume that there is a linear relationship between trees and monkeys.

Figure 8.1

Trees ⟶ Monkeys

Figure 8.2

(A)

(B)

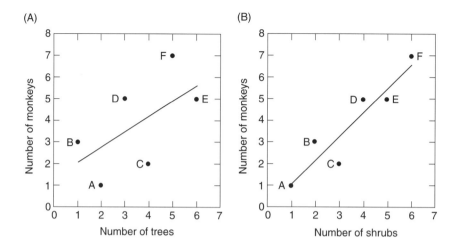

Adding Things Together

The graph that illustrates the relationship between monkeys and trees (Figure 8.2A) does appear to be linear and shows an increase in monkey density with tree density. This relationship appears logical because monkeys take refuge from ground predators in trees. If we collect data on the density of a species of shrub that the monkeys use for food, we also find a positive linear relationship (Figure 8.2B). These two graphs suggest the flow chart in Figure 8.3.

Based on these graphs, students usually suggest that planting trees and shrubs is a good way to increase monkey numbers. Actually, this is inappropriate given the data in hand, and it is not a question of whether there is sufficient replication. If we analyze the data by the technique of least-squares regression, we can produce dispersion graphs that illustrate the partial effects of shrubs independent of trees, and trees independent of shrubs. To see how this is done, we first have to look at four intermediate graphs (Figure 8.4).

The upper case letters indicate the reserve from which the data came. The vertical lines from the points to the lines indicate the variability in each dependent

Figure 8.3

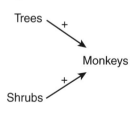

variable not explained by the linear model. From Figure 8.4A, we can obtain the variability in monkeys that is not associated with shrubs (represented by the vertical lines). The differences between the data and the model, called "deviations" or "residuals," reflect changes in the number of monkeys due to factors other than shrubs. Likewise, from Figure 8.4B we can obtain the variability in trees not associated with shrubs. If we plot the residuals from these regressions against shrubs, we find that these residuals show no relation-

Figure 8.4

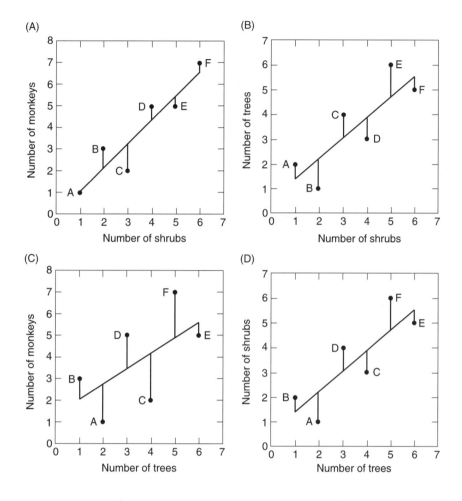

ship to shrubs. Some authors say that they describe the variability expected if shrubs were kept constant.

If we plot the residuals from Figure 8.4A against the residuals from Figure 8.4B, and pair them by reserve, we get the expected relationship between monkeys and trees if we remove the effect of shrubs or, equivalently, the relationship expected if the number of shrubs is constant among reserves (Figure 8.5A).

Figure 8.5A is the partial regression of monkeys on trees. It is called a partial regression because it only shows that part of the variability in the data not associated with shrubs. The process is completely general and we can use the residuals from Figures 8.4C and 8.4D to plot the partial regression of monkeys on shrubs independent of trees (Figure 8.5B). In fact, the method of multiple regression uses

Figure 8.5

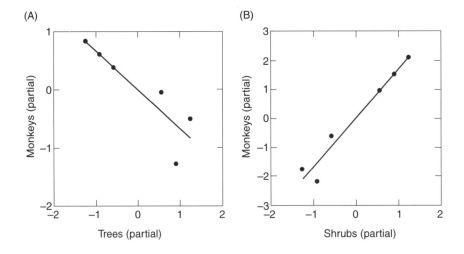

(A)

(B)

the partial regressions to isolate the probable effect of each factor independent of how many other factors are in the model.

Adding Partitioned Variability

This process of partitioning variance among several factors appears complicated at first, but it is not a complication imposed for purely cultural reasons. It helps us see more clearly. The simple relationship between monkeys and trees (see Figure 8.2A) is positive, leading most researchers to assume that trees are probably good for monkeys. However, the partial regression (see Figure 8.5A) indicates a negative effect of trees on monkeys if we statistically hold the shrubs constant. In the absence of other information, we should certainly not embark on a tree-planting scheme. In fact, if the hypothesis suggested in Figure 8.5A is corroborated, we may even start cutting trees in order to increase the number of monkeys.

The process illustrated in this example is general, and illustrates the way that analysis of variance, or other modeling techniques, can be used to reveal patterns that are not obvious in our original simple dispersion graphs. It did this by producing another dispersion graph. Mathematically, we have reduced the descriptive model of the form $Y = a + b_1 \times X_1 + b_2 \times X_2 + e$ to two models of the form $Y_{\text{Partial}} = a + b \times X_{\text{Partial}} + e$.

Please note that the partial plots, and not the mathematical summary or the P values, are the real results of the analysis. The statistics may be used as an adjunct to the plots, but can never replace them. You may find our example overly simplified. However, even very complex real-world problems are profitably attacked by partitioning variance within a model (Polis 1999).

The equations for the multiple regression and the partial regressions are telling us the same story. The overall equation for our example is:

$$\text{Monkeys} = 0.33 - 0.667 \times \text{Trees} + 1.667 \times \text{Shrubs}$$

The partial regressions are the following:

$$\text{Monkeys (partial)} = 0.0 - 0.667 \times \text{Trees (partial)}$$

$$\text{Monkeys (partial)} = 0.0 + 1.667 \times \text{Shrubs (partial)}$$

The overall regression has the same inclinations (b values) as the partial regressions. In fact, it is constructed by summing the partial regressions. The elevation is not the same, as it is a single value that substitutes for the individual values from the partial regressions. The similarity of the overall regression to the partial regressions illustrates its essential nature.

> **A multiple regression is simply the sum of the linear effects estimated by the partial regressions.**

This is a very simple model, but it has proved useful in many situations.

Checking Assumptions with Partial Plots

Researchers frequently calculate the probability that the effect (b value) of the independent variables is zero, or some other value (the null hypothesis). We will not go into details here, but the principles of testing a null hypothesis of $b = 0$ are similar to testing the null hypothesis of DIF = 0. These probabilities can be calculated by randomization tests or by parametric tests such as the t-test.

It is important to do the parametric tests on the overall multiple regression, and not on the individual partial regressions. This is because the computer will not know how many other factors, and hence parameters, were used to calculate the partials. Since the number of degrees of freedom is calculated from the number of independent observations minus the number of parameters estimated, the computer will use the wrong degrees of freedom if it does not know how many parameters were estimated.

In our experience, the most common source of significant P values in multiple regression is the inclusion of a single point that was registered on the wrong scale, perhaps in millimeters instead of in centimeters. This point does not stand out on the simple regressions, but becomes obvious in the partial plots. See Anscombe (1973) for examples that apply equally to simple regressions and partial plots.

In any case, never attempt to interpret the probabilities without looking at the partial plots.

Partial plots are also used to verify the other assumptions of multiple regression, such as that the relationships are linear and that the variability is constant along the line. If inspection of the partial plots indicates that something is wrong and you have to either transform data (see Chapter 11), or delete or correct an observation, the whole analysis has to be repeated, including checking the partial plots. As the technique is based on analysis of residuals around relationships, changing one relationship changes all the others in the analysis. If you can't fix the problems, you may have to look to other techniques, such as limit regression (Cade et al. 1999).

If the variables are autocorrelated (the observations are not independent), the analysis will identify many more significant variables than actually exist (Lennon 2000). Therefore, none of the checks given above will be of any use unless the data are collected correctly (no pseudoreplication).

Analyses of categorical variables obey the same principles, though most textbooks have separate sections for continuous variables (regression), categorical variables (analysis of variance, ANOVA) and mixtures of categorical and continuous variables (analysis of covariance, ANCOVA). All of these could be called analysis of variance but most books do not emphasize the similarities.

Figure 8.6

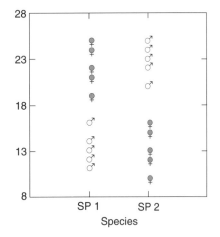

Species

Interactions

In this chapter, we assume that the variation due to several independent variables can be added to give the overall variation. However, this is not always true. Figure 8.6 illustrates a situation in which the effects of two independent variables cancel each other out.

In this example, there is no simple effect of species because the average heights of the two species, without regard to sex, are the same. Similarly, the average heights of the sexes, without regard to species are equal. However, within species, there is an obvious effect of sex, and within each sex, there is a strong effect of species. If we add the simple effects of sex and species (both of which are approximately zero) to the variability within each sex by species by category (the residual), we do not get the total variability, which is much greater. Mathematically, this is represented by the following inequality:

$$V_{\text{Factor1}} + V_{\text{Factor2}} + V_{\text{Residual}} < V_{\text{Total}}$$

However, we can invent a phantom factor, called an interaction term, to make the equation balance:

$$V_{\text{Factor1}} + V_{\text{Factor2}} + V_{\text{Residual}} + V_{\text{Interaction}} = V_{\text{Total}}$$

An interaction indicates that the effect of one (or more) factors depends on the levels of other factors. Interactions can also occur between continuous variables, and between continuous variables and categorical variables. They are more often studied with categorical variables because many computer programs automatically give all possible interactions for ANOVA. However, this is not always sensible, and we will discuss variable selection in the following chapter.

In terms of our conceptual flow chart, the presence of an interaction indicates that we have left out some important variable(s). Discovering interactions is not an interesting exercise in itself. However, interactions are valuable signs that we need to rethink our flow chart so that we can understand why the interaction occurs.

Remember that F-ratios are constructed from mean squares, which are compound variances (see Chapter 6). In order to work out what variances are included in each mean square we must take into account whether the factors are fixed or random. Many computer programs will ask if the factors are fixed or random, and calculate the correct F-ratios. However, if you do the calculations by hand, or use a program that does not ask whether the factors are fixed, you have to consult an appropriate textbook. Mathematically minded readers can consult Winer et al. (1991) to learn how to construct the correct F-ratios. Zar (1996) has an appendix that shows how to do it without having to understand the process.

Many conclusions in ecological literature are based on incorrect analyses because the researchers analyzed the data as though all of the factors were fixed (Bennington and Thayne 1994, Newman et al. 1997). Review Chapter 7 to see why this model is very restrictive. We will not dwell on these statistical points because if the data are collected correctly, any statistician can help set up the analysis. However, it is important to realize that mixed–model ANOVA can be very weak unless you have large numbers of replicates and large numbers of levels of the random factor so that meaningful estimates of the variance due to level sampling can be made. Koele (1982) said, "Experiments that have random factors with only two or three levels must be considered as absurd as t-tests on samples with two or three observations."

## CHAPTER 9

"Only include factors in your analysis that are justified by common sense."

Which Variables Should I Analyze Statistically?

This is one of the most common questions asked by students, and it is a question that should be asked more frequently by practicing researchers. The simplest answer is to include all of the variables in your statistical analysis that you include in your flow chart. However, variables should only be included in the flow chart if their inclusion is strongly based on theory, common sense, or natural history information. We do not want to include too many variables, especially if they do not contribute information about the dependent variable. Remember that we lose one degree of freedom for each parameter estimated (see Chapter 5).

We calculated the relationship between crayfish density and an index of pollution in twelve sites. The analysis indicates that the null hypothesis—that there was no relationship between crayfish density and pollution—is very unlikely ($P = 0.014$). This is strong evidence for an effect of pollution on crayfish. We then added six random variables, one at a time, to the analysis. Figure 9.1 shows the effect of adding the spurious variables on the proportion of the variance explained (solid line) and the probability that the model conforms to the null hypothesis (dashed line), both expressed as percentages.

After the addition of the third random variable, the regression is no longer considered significant at 0.05 (5%). The extra variables increase the proportion

Figure 9.1

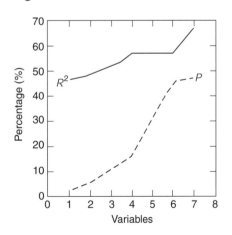

of the variance apparently explained by the regression, but this is a trivial result as the variables added were generated by a random-number generator. This is the general pattern expected when the number of variables is high in relation to the number of independent observations (sites in this case). However, you could get lucky, and the addition of random variables could increase the "significance" of the regression. This would be basing your interpretation on the vagaries of the mathematics.

In general, the addition of irrelevant variables will only compromise your biological interpretations.

> **A good rule of thumb is to work out how many replicates you can reasonably collect, divide that number by 10, and try to restrict hypothesis tests to approximately that number of variables.**

In any case, avoid designs that will result in less than 10 degrees of freedom in the residual (Green, 1989). Harris (1975) suggested that multiple regression is not robust to violations of assumptions about the normal distribution of residuals unless there are at least 50 more observations than there are independent variables!

In the following section, we will see how some researchers use the computer to reduce the number of variables. The philosophy of selecting variables has much in common with the philosophy of multiple comparisons, and Tukey's (1991) article is a good place to start to understand the different sorts of questions that can be asked about the real world.

Artificial Intelligence

Statistical methods are not efficient at sorting through lots of measurements to find out what is related to what. To understand this, we consider the sorts of results produced by some automated variable selection schemes. For the following exercises, we will only use data produced by the computer's random-number generator. Therefore, there are no causal relationships among the variables, and the correlations are exactly those that are expected by chance.

One of the most common automated variable selection schemes is stepwise regression. There are a number of variants on this, including step-up, step-down, and best-subsets regression. Practitioners defend one or other as being "better" than the others even though there is often little difference (Berk 1978). However, our point is that the probabilities associated with the results of any of them cannot be related to any known null hypothesis (e.g., Freedman 1983, James and McCulloch 1990, Anderson et al. 2001). They are therefore pseudoprobabilities and should not be presented as anything else.

If a technique is used to just generate hypotheses, there is no reason to present the pseudoprobabilities, which have no logical interpretation. We can guarantee that consulting with a competent biologist is a much better way to generate hypotheses. This is because you must know something about the relationships among the "independent" variables before you put them into your analysis (see Chapter 10). For the sake of illustration, we imagine that you have a detailed knowledge of the relationships among the independent variables, but cannot generate a hypothesis as to which ones are likely to affect the dependent variable.

Table 9.1 was generated by our computer using the SYSTAT 8 statistical package. These are the results of a conventional regression analysis relating the density of crayfish to 10 potential independent variables. We have given them realistic names, but remember that we generated them in a random-number generator.

Don't worry if you do not understand most of the table now. The last column gives the probabilities that each of the variables (listed in the first column) conform to the null hypothesis. None of them is significant at 0.05. This is expected since the analysis was based on random variables. However, we would not have been surprised if one or two of the 10 probabilities had been less than 0.05

Table 9.1

Dep Var: CRAYFISH   N: 14   Multiple R: 0.928   Squared multiple R: 0.860
Adjusted squared multiple R: 0.395   Standard error of estimate: 0.235

Effect	Coefficient	Std Error	Std Coef	Tolerance	t	P(2 Tail)
CONSTANT	0.941	0.627	0.000	.	1.500	0.231
VELOCITY	−0.131	0.520	−0.108	0.256	−0.253	0.817
TEMPERATURE	−0.122	0.401	−0.109	0.361	−0.304	0.781
DEPTH	0.320	0.345	0.289	0.477	0.926	0.423
WIDTH	−0.428	0.328	−0.421	0.448	−1.305	0.283
COVER	0.140	0.482	0.134	0.221	0.291	0.790
SNAGS	−0.645	0.308	−0.732	0.380	−2.092	0.128
ROCKS	0.069	0.378	0.071	0.311	0.184	0.866
HERONS	−0.057	0.454	−0.056	0.236	−0.126	0.907
CARNFISH	−0.212	0.438	−0.177	0.347	−0.484	0.661
HERBFISH	0.359	0.263	0.368	0.640	1.363	0.266

Analysis of Variance

Source	Sum-of-Squares	df	Mean-Square	F-ratio	P
Regression	1.024	10	0.102	1.848	0.335
Residual	0.166	3	0.055		

because, at this level of significance, we expect about one in 20 to appear significant when the null hypothesis is correct. The analysis of variance section at the bottom of the table indicates that the overall probability that the model conforms to the null hypothesis is 0.335. This is reassuring because we know that the data conform exactly to the null hypothesis.

We used the stepwise option in the same program to select the "best" variables from the same data file. Some programs, like the SYSTAT program, present the pseudoprobabilities as P in inverted commas and do not give a probability for the overall regression. However, many programs are not as honest, so we re-ran the analysis including only the variables identified by the stepwise regression. Now, the three variables included are highly "significant." In fact, the pseudoprobability indicates that there are only two chances in 1000 that snags conform to some null hypothesis, and the analysis of variance indicates that the probability that the overall regression conforms to some null hypothesis is about three in 1000 (Table 9.2). We know that the data conformed to the conventional null hypothesis (no relation between independent and dependent variables), so we have no idea to what null hypotheses these pseudoprobabilities relate.

There is no reason to present the results of stepwise regressions in publications. Hypotheses based on expert opinions would be much more useful, and few readers understand that the pseudoprobabilities presented are not probabilities in any conventional sense. Not only do the statistics presented in Table 9.2 not relate in any meaningful way to the results in Table 9.1, there are also many other combinations of variables that could describe the data equally well. Table 9.3 shows the "best" model obtained by stepwise regression if we adjust one of the options of

Table 9.2

Dep Var: LAGOSTIN   N: 14   Multiple R: 0.856   Squared multiple R: 0.733
Adjusted squared multiple R: 0.653   Standard error of estimate: 0.178

Effect	Coefficient	Std Error	Std Coef	Tolerance	t	P(2 Tail)
CONSTANT	0.951	0.135	0.000	.	7.045	0.000
WIDTH	−0.448	0.166	−0.440	0.996	−2.690	0.023
SNAGS	−0.592	0.145	−0.672	0.989	−4.095	0.002
HERBFISH	0.406	0.160	0.416	0.993	2.536	0.030

	Analysis of Variance				
Source	Sum-of-Squares	df	Mean-Square	F-ratio	P
Regression	1.873	3	0.291	9.165	0.003
Residual	0.317	10	0.032		

Table 9.3

Dep Var: LAGOSTIN   N: 14   Multiple R: 0.888   Squared multiple R: 0.789
Adjusted squared multiple R: 0.695   Standard error of estimate: 0.167

Effect	Coefficient	Std Error	Std Coef	Tolerance	t	P(2 Tail)
CONSTANT	1.122	0.168	0.000	.	6.659	0.000
WIDTH	−0.349	0.169	−0.343	0.853	−2.071	0.068
SNAGS	−0.628	0.138	−0.713	0.962	−1.537	0.001
CARNFISH	−0.339	0.221	−0.284	0.689	−1.537	0.159
HERBFISH	0.294	0.167	0.301	0.804	1.764	0.111

		Analysis of Variance			
Source	Sum-of-Squares	df	Mean-Square	F-ratio	P
Regression	0.939	4	0.235	8.402	0.004
Residual	0.251	9	0.028		

the analysis by a very small amount. It is the same analysis except that we change the *P* value to enter or remove variables from the model from 0.15 to 0.2, which is the default value used in many other programs.

The model now includes another variable, and the pseudoprobabilities have changed drastically. Changing other options or using another stepping procedure can change the "best" model even more drastically. If you use the computer to think for you, wait until you have data to test its hypotheses before you publish them.

It should be obvious that including spurious variables in the analysis can be as damaging as leaving out an important variable.

Measuring everything and "letting the data speak for themselves" is not an efficient way to discover things.

For this reason, most journals require that researchers test hypotheses. If every researcher published every hypothesis they generated without testing them, the literature would increase a thousandfold, and communication would reduce by an equal amount (see Platt 1964).

Untested hypotheses should only be published if they promise to produce a paradigm shift (Kuhn 1970). Harris (1975) stated that "Statistics is a form of social control over the professional behavior of researchers. The ultimate justification of any statistical procedure lies in the kinds of research behavior it encourages or discourages." From this point of view, stepwise procedures generally encourage anti-social behavior.

Computer Generated Phantom Variables

Computer programs can trick us into thinking that we do not have to use common sense when considering what variables to investigate. However, they can also create spurious variables. The models we have considered so far did not investigate any interactions (see Chapter 8 if you have forgotten what an interaction is). However, many analysis of variance programs automatically generate all possible interactions whether you wanted them or not. Consider the results obtained by a researcher who carried out a controlled experiment to test the effects of five factors on the density of crayfish, using two levels per factor. The researcher, a graduate student, is appalled that none of the factors his supervisor suggested are significant (Table 9.4). Therefore, the researcher decides to test for all possible interactions (Table 9.5).

> **ANOVA tables are interpreted from the bottom up.**

If a factor is involved in an interaction, all terms above and including that factor, are presumably significant. Researchers sometimes conclude that the simple effect of a factor that is involved in an interaction is not significant. This is illogical. If the factor is involved in an interaction, there is no simple effect. The effect of that factor depends on the levels of one or more other factors.

Based on Table 9.5, the researcher concludes that there is a significant interaction ($P = 0.001$) between snags and herbivorous fish, and therefore that snags and

Table 9.4

Dep Var: LAGOSTIN   N: 96   Multiple R: 0.196   Squared multiple R: 0.038

Source	Sum-of-Squares	df	Mean-Square	F-ratio	P
		Analysis of Variance			
DEPTH	0.130	1	0.130	1.596	0.210
SNAGS	0.120	1	0.120	1.468	0.229
VELOCITY	0.010	1	0.010	0.119	0.731
HERBFISH	0.032	1	0.032	0.396	0.531
CARNFISH	0.000	1	0.000	0.001	0.974
ERROR	7.354	90	0.082		

Table 9.5

Dep Var: LAGOSTIN   N: 96   Multiple R: 0.629   Squared multiple R: 0.395

Source	Analysis of Variance Sum-of-Squares	df	Mean-Square	F-ratio	P
DEPTH	0.130	1	0.130	1.804	0.184
SNAGS	0.120	1	0.120	1.659	0.202
VELOCITY	0.010	1	0.010	0.135	0.715
HERBFISH	0.032	1	0.032	0.448	0.506
CARNFISH	0.000	1	0.000	0.001	0.973
DEPTH*SNAGS	0.067	1	0.067	0.923	0.340
DEPTH*VELOCITY	0.092	1	0.092	1.267	0.265
DEPTH*HERBFISH	0.231	1	0.231	3.199	0.078
DEPTH*CARNFISH	0.025	1	0.025	0.341	0.561
SNAGS*VELOCITY	0.001	1	0.001	0.015	0.903
SNAGS*HERBFISH	0.956	1	0.956	13.223	0.001
SNAGS*CARNFISH	0.046	1	0.046	0.643	0.426
VELOCITY*HERBFISH	0.023	1	0.023	0.321	0.573
VELOCITY*CARNFISH	0.036	1	0.036	0.503	0.481
HERBFISH*CARNFISH	0.017	1	0.017	0.240	0.626
DEPTH*SNAGS *VELOCITY	0.087	1	0.087	1.202	0.277
DEPTH*SNAGS *HERBFISH	0.022	1	0.022	0.309	0.580
DEPTH*SNAGS *CARNFISH	0.123	1	0.123	1.700	0.197
DEPTH*VELOCITY *HERBFISH	0.231	1	0.231	3.194	0.079
DEPTH*VELOCITY *CARNFISH	0.129	1	0.129	1.785	0.186
DEPTH*HERBFISH *CARNFISH	0.003	1	0.003	0.040	0.843
SNAGS*VELOCITY *HERBFISH	0.051	1	0.051	0.710	0.403
SNAGS*VELOCITY *CARNFISH	0.103	1	0.103	1.424	0.237
SNAGS*HERBFISH *CARNFISH	0.007	1	0.007	0.093	0.761
VELOCITY*HERBFISH *CARNFISH	0.099	1	0.099	1.366	0.247
DEPTH*SNAGS *VELOCITY*HERBFISH	0.006	1	0.006	0.088	0.768
DEPTH*SNAGS *VELOCITY*CARNFISH	0.000	1	0.000	0.000	0.984
DEPTH*SNAGS *HERBFISH*CARNFISH	0.113	1	0.113	1.557	0.217
DEPTH*VELOCITY *HERBFISH*CARNFISH	0.014	1	0.014	0.187	0.667
SNAGS*VELOCITY *HERBFISH*CARNFISH	0.115	1	0.115	1.597	0.211
DEPTH*SNAGS *VELOCITY*HERBFISH *CARNFISH	0.131	1	0.131	1.817	0.182
Error	4.626	64	0.072		

herbivorous fish affect crayfish densities. There are many biological explanations for an interaction between snags and herbivorous fish and this allows for an expanded discussion in the student's thesis. The student also considers the probability of the null hypothesis that there is no interaction among depth, velocity, and herbivorous fish to be sufficiently low ($P = 0.079$) to warrant a discussion of the possible importance of those factors.

The researcher and his supervisor are happy, but has science been advanced? The example was again based on random data. There are 25 possible effects or interaction terms in an ANOVA with five factors. We therefore expect about one result to be "significant" at the 0.05 level for random data. However, the interactions involve more than one factor, so we expect more than one factor to be "significant." The student was almost guaranteed to have "significant" results, even for random data.

Many authors do not seem to realize that standard ANOVA programs do not control the overall error rate (e.g., Fowler 1990). Many types of statistical tables present large numbers of tests, and do not control the overall error rate (Rice 1989). Harris (1975) points out that multiple regression programs usually present a significance test of the overall regression, but categorical ANOVA programs do not. This is strange, as an insignificant overall test combined with significant partial effects is a good indication that we have included too many variables in the model, and that the statistical "significance" is an artifact in both regression and ANOVA.

It is important to identify interactions when they occur in our models, principally because they indicate that we should be including other factors, or we should be reconsidering the scales on which the variables were measured. However, if we allow the computer to generate all possible interactions without thought as to which might be the most appropriate, we will end up generating many spurious relationships, sending other researchers off on wild goose chases. Researchers who are mathematically very competent may use mathematics to help decide among candidate models (e.g., Burnham and Anderson 1998).

> **However, the researcher is never relieved of the burden of using logic to decide which variables should be included.**

Doing this well is the art of the scientist.

Sometimes, we want to collect data to construct hypotheses and data to test the hypotheses at the same time. In this case, we need a lot of data, but we can divide the data bank into exploratory and validation subsets. Exploratory data sets usually result in statistics that are overly optimistic with regard to predictive ability

(Picard and Cook 1984). If the validation subset is representative of the exploratory sample, and both are representative of the population of interest, this process can save time and money. Science works by testing whether results are repeatable. Validation subsets are not as good evidence as substantive replication (Guttman 1985). This is repetition in another place by another researcher. However, validation subsets are often the best that we can do.

The general problem of not reporting insignificant tests extends to comparisons among studies, interpretation of literature reviews, and the statistical technique of meta-analysis (Palmer 1999, Thornhill et al. 1999). In all of these situations, the researcher has to ask what was tested but not reported. However, we will not deal any further with those issues here.

## CHAPTER 10

*"Statistical tests cannot be interpreted
without a flow chart."*

More Complex Models: How to String Things Together

Thus far, we have been considering how to analyze very simple situations in which the independent variables can affect the dependent variable but they cannot affect each other. Obviously, this is not very realistic. In this chapter, we continue to deal with simple linear relationships but we will allow the independent variables to affect each other. There are other approaches to determining the overall importance of variables (see MacNally 2002), but the results of such analyses should be interpreted in relation to flow charts. We will investigate the example given in Chapter 2. The flow chart (Figure 10.1) shows the direction of influence, but we have not considered what flows along those arrows.

In Table 10.1 we present data for 30 lakes where four variables were measured simultaneously. "Pollution" represents heavy metal concentration in parts per billion, "Fish" is measured as the mean number of fish per gill-net hour, "Phytoplankton" is the concentration of chlorophyll relative to a standard, and "Crayfish" is the number of crayfish captured per trap hour.
When we deal with simple relationships, these different scales of measurement do not matter. We can say things like "One unit increase in pollution leads to so many units decrease in the number of crayfish." However, if the effects of pollution on phytoplankton are measured in units of heavy metals, and the effects of phytoplankton on crayfish are measured in terms of chlorophyll, the same effect cannot flow along both of the lower arrows in our flow chart.

Figure 10.1

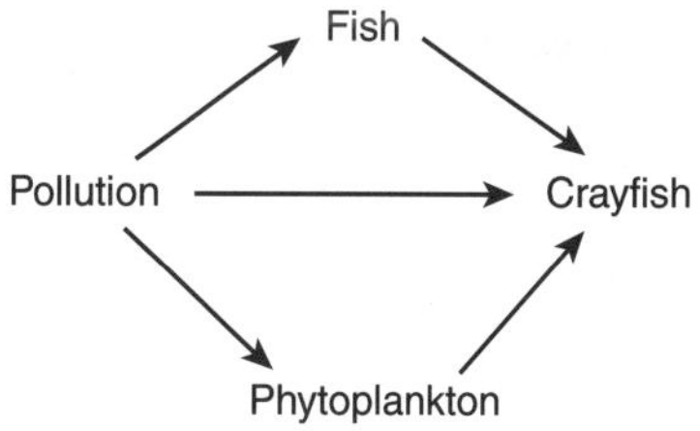

Table 10.1

Pollution	Fish	Phytoplankton	Crayfish
9.5	9.0	12.5	2.4
8.5	9.9	11.6	5.0
9.2	9.1	15.3	5.8
10.3	8.0	13.9	6.2
9.6	9.1	14.4	3.6
10.9	5.6	14.2	5.2
10.7	4.3	15.1	8.1
8.9	6.2	12.0	3.4
10.5	6.2	14.2	4.4
9.0	7.9	14.3	4.0
9.8	8.0	15.4	4.7
8.0	8.0	11.1	3.4
9.0	8.7	12.7	4.0
9.8	5.4	12.9	6.9
10.8	6.1	15.8	6.4
9.2	8.0	13.3	3.4
10.4	7.5	14.2	4.0
9.4	7.5	16.0	9.1
8.6	10.2	14.2	6.8
9.8	6.8	13.3	6.5
8.7	8.3	12.0	5.8
8.8	7.9	12.5	4.4
9.8	7.8	15.3	6.1
8.2	9.5	13.0	3.5
9.9	6.6	15.7	9.3
8.7	7.0	14.3	5.1
8.9	7.7	13.0	3.0
10.0	8.3	15.1	4.8
8.1	9.8	14.4	3.0
10.2	7.3	15.7	6.3

To put all of the variables on the same scale, we divide each value of each variable by the standard deviation of that variable, as Student did to remove the problem of scale from the t-statistic. The original data and the standard deviation have the same dimensions, so when we divide one by the other we have an apparently dimensionless quantity (the units in the numerator and denominator cancel).

Do not worry if you do not understand the algebra. Effectively, by dividing by the standard deviation we are putting all of the measurements in units of standard deviations. We can say things like "An increase of one standard deviation in pollution leads to a decrease of so many standard deviations in the number of crayfish."

> **When we calculate statistics based on standardized data, they are called standardized estimates of parameters.**

Most computer programs provide the standardized estimates of parameters but, in general, they are of little use unless you want to see how effects propagate through flow diagrams.

Use of standardized coefficients to evaluate chains of effects is called path analysis (or structural equation modeling). We will demonstrate a simple method of path analysis so you will better understand the concept. (We also refer you to literature that explains the currently accepted methods.)

Before you become too involved in the mathematics, it is important that you grasp some concepts that relate to the differences between direct, indirect, and overall effects. These concepts must be understood in order to develop effective sampling

designs and to make it possible to collect the data necessary for structural equation modeling.

Estimating Direct Effects

First, we analyze the data using a standard multiple
regression analysis but report the standardized regression coefficients. These are dimensionless and we can
use them to evaluate the relative contributions of the independent variables to the
observed variation in the dependent variable.

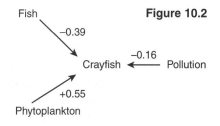

Figure 10.2

$$\text{Crayfish} = 0.0 - 0.16 \times \text{Pollution} - 0.39 \times \text{Fish} + 0.55 \times \text{Phytoplankton}$$

We can represent this in the flow chart, and assign the values of the standardized coefficients to represent the strength of each relationship (Figure 10.2). In this
context, these values are called path coefficients.

Based on the multiple regression, the effect of pollution is negative and its magnitude (0.16) is much less than those of fish (0.39) and phytoplankton (0.55).
Statistically, there does not appear to be a significant effect of pollution ($P = 0.53$)
but there is some evidence for an effect of fish ($P = 0.07$) and a strong indication of
an effect of phytoplankton ($P = 0.01$). This is counterintuitive, because there are
generally more crayfish in lakes with more pollution and a simple regression indicates a significant ($P = 0.03$) positive effect of pollution on crayfish with a magnitude of 0.41.

Simple regressions can be misleading (see Chapter 8). However, we can see that
the path diagram represented by the multiple regression (see Figure 10.2) does not
represent the system as we believe it to function (see Figure 10.1). Figure 10.2 is in
the form of a star, with the arrows approaching the dependent variable from all
angles. The direction of the arrows is quite arbitrary because the independent
variables do not affect each other. Systems that can be represented by star flow
charts are very rare in ecology, but most of the commonly used statistical procedures assume a star flow chart.

> **That is why we must construct a flow chart that represents the way we
> believe the system functions before we choose an analysis.**

The multiple regression is telling us that if fish and phytoplankton were held constant, the effect of pollution on crayfish would be negative and possibly not significant. This is called a direct effect. The problem is that, in the real world, it is not
possible to maintain fish and phytoplankton densities constant when this type of

pollution varies. Perhaps if we removed all of the fish and phytoplankton from the lakes, we could see the effect predicted by the multiple regression, but this is hardly feasible or ethically justifiable.

Knowledge of direct effects is sometimes useful in fields such as medicine or agriculture where it is possible to manipulate some factors beyond their naturally occurring levels, and eliminate or severely control others. When we do not have such control, it is often more useful to know the real effect of a factor and not its hypothetical effect if everything else were constant.

Estimating Indirect Effects

We can use path analysis to investigate indirect as well as direct effects. The standardized regression coefficients tell us the hypothetical direct effects of the variables that have arrows leading directly to crayfish (Figure 10.3). Note that the direct effects of variables affecting crayfish in Figure 10.3 are the same as those in Figure 10.2. There are also direct effects of pollution on fish and of pollution on phytoplankton.

We can obtain the standardized regressions for these paths by simple regression. To calculate the indirect effects, we multiply the path coefficients along the paths. To obtain the overall effect of a variable, we add its direct and indirect effects.

For pollution we can look at the following paths and their corresponding path coefficients:

Pollution → Crayfish	− 0.16
Pollution→ Fish → Crayfish	+ 0.26
Pollution → Phytoplankton → Crayfish	+ 0.31

The overall effect (sum of the direct and indirect effects) of pollution is 0.41, which is the result we obtained by directly regressing crayfish on pollution. Although the simple regression gives the correct numerical answer, it implies a direct effect of pollution on crayfish that probably does not exist. The multiple regression gives the correct answer with regard to the direct effects, but it is an answer about a world that we do not believe can exist. In our model, pollution is driving the system, even though it has only a very weak direct effect.

It is a disturbing aspect of the conventional analyses that they tend to discount the ultimate effects, and focus on the proximal causes which are really only the result of the more important variables on the left of the model.

Figure 10.3

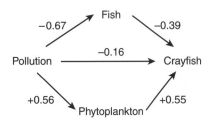

Manipulative experiments, in which the researcher maintains some variables constant, or produces combinations of levels of factors that do not exist in nature, have the same limitation. They are reporting on direct effects expected in an imaginary world. Path analysis allows us to interpret analyses in a biologically meaningful way. Without flow charts, statistical analyses are generally non-interpretable.

Some Problems with Path Analysis

We have made path analyses seem very attractive. However, there are some serious limitations (Petraitis et al. 1996, Shipley 1999). We used a path analysis only to illustrate the first step toward dealing with more ecologically realistic models. The analyses generally assume linear relationships, no loops in the flow chart, and are based on standard deviations. Therefore, if you have not sampled the real variability for each variable in the system, the path coefficients do not give the expected effects.

> **For this reason it is difficult to interpret path analyses when researchers have experimentally manipulated some variables (Petraitis et al. 1996).**

Also, some researchers consider that the use of simple standardized regression coefficients is not correct unless the analysis includes all possible paths (Petraitis et al. 1996). For instance, we did not include a path from fish to phytoplankton because we had no evidence for such a causal link. If you have not included all possible paths, and believe that this is a problem, you can fool the computer by modifying the matrix the computer uses to calculate the multiple regressions, or use a maximum-likelihood program designed specifically for structural equation modeling (Petraitis et al. 1996). We give a brief introduction to the concept of maximum-likelihood methods in Chapter 11, but this is a very complex subject that most researchers avoid, and few biologists are likely to have the mathematical background and computer skills to try to fool the computer. In general, the use of standardized regression coefficients give similar results to the more sophisticated methods, and limits on sample sizes and independence of observations are generally more important than the method used to calculate the coefficients.

Categorical variables can be put into the model if they have only two levels, or if their levels can be placed in an ordered series. However, interpretating a variable whose distribution can not be described by its standard deviation is difficult. In these cases, it may be necessary to use very complex maximum-likelihood methods.

Sometimes, path analyses may not be good at revealing patterns that can be shown by other evidence, though some form of path analysis will probably always be necessary when analyzing over multiple scales (see O'Neill and King [1998] for an overview of scale problems). Therefore, although we suggest that all statistical analyses first require inspection of a flow chart, you should only consider applying structural equation modeling if you are dealing with a relatively simple system. You should also have a very good computer program, and a tame statistician to get you out of the mathematical mess you will almost certainly end up in.

In this book, as in most books, we have concentrated on the analysis of variance techniques because this is a good place to start and the concepts are simple. However, Guttman (1985) commented, "This is not unlike giving a child a toy hammer: he will use it on all objects in sight." The difficulty of estimating parameters is related to a general class of approaches called "inverse problems" (Wood 1997).

If you decide to analyze the flow chart mathematically, you should also consider the possibility of using computer intensive simulations (see Starfield and Bleloch 1991) or other complex mathematical techniques (see McCune and Grace 2002, Link 1999, Spitz and Leks 1999, Wardle 1998, and Burnham and Anderson 1998).

All of these things are far beyond the scope of this introduction, and require the help of a very competent statistician.

We hope that we have at least presented an idea of why some researchers do not use the standard statistical techniques that have become the "badge" of practicing ecologists. In Chapter 12, we will describe some aspects of multivariate analyses, which at first sight are a biologist's nightmare and a mathematician's paradise, and try to present them in a similar style to the rest of this book. However, in the next chapter we will return to analyses with only one independent variable to describe methods other than linear least-squares. Although the mathematics can get complicated, it is important to keep in mind that we have gone back to analyzing simple relationships that have only one dependent and one independent variable. Most of these could be replaced by simple graphs.

## CHAPTER 11

"Least-squares methods are theoretically appropriate only under a very restrictive set of conditions."

Straightening the World: Transformations and Other Tricks

Our analyses so far have been based on linear models in which we minimized squared deviations to estimate parameters. These algebraic least-squares methods are theoretically appropriate only under a very restrictive set of conditions. They assume that the relationships are linear, the effects are additive, the residuals from the models are normally distributed, there is no stochastic (random) error in the measurement of the independent variables, the variance in the dependent variable is distributed homogeneously across all levels of the independent variables, and other unlikely conditions. When these conditions are not met, some other model is a better estimator.

We will first consider some of the ways of transforming data to conform to the least-squares models, and then look at some alternative models. Our models are very simple and we do not attempt to give a comprehensive treatment of the techniques. Rather, we highlight some of the conceptual issues associated with these techniques so that they can be used to reveal, instead of obscure, patterns.

Our example concerns an ecologist who is trying to estimate the biomass of a large area of forest. If you prefer an applied example, imagine a forester attempting to estimate wood volume. Similar techniques are used by fisheries biologists to estimate the condition from length and mass measurements of fish, and physiologists confront such problems when mass affects the variables that they are interested in. In fact, there are theoretical reasons to expect this type of relationship to be common in biological and engineering systems (Carlson and Doyle 1999).

Figure 11.1

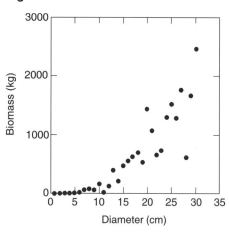

It is relatively easy to take diameter measurements of trees. However, biomass estimation methods are difficult and destructive to the trees. The ecologist therefore decides to determine the relationship between diameter and biomass for 30 trees, and uses this relationship to predict biomass from diameter measurements taken over the whole area of interest. The data for the 30 trees is shown in Figure 11.1.

The relationship is not linear and the variability in biomass increases as diameter increases. It is not possible to produce a predictive equation using algebraic least-squares with the raw data. However, the relationship is likely to conform to a power function of the following form:

$$\text{Biomass} = a \times \text{Diameter}^b + e_1$$

Here a and b are parameters that describe the shape and position of the curve, and e_1 represents variation not explained by the model. Taking logs of both sides of the equation (but disregarding the error term) results in a form of linear equation that can be handled by ordinary least-squares algebra:

$$\log(\text{Biomass}) = \log(a) + b \times \log(\text{Diameter}) + e_2$$

Therefore, the biologist decides to transform the data, putting both axes on $\log_{10}$ scales (Figure 11.2). The relationship is now linear, and the variability in biomass is similar throughout the range of values of diameter. This facilitates the mathematics and allows the biologist to use least-squares algebra. We leave the problem, that this implies a multiplicative error term in the original equation, to the statisticians.

The line can be described by the following equation:

$$\log_{10}(\text{Biomass}) = -0.775 + 2.778 \times \log_{10}(\text{Diameter})$$

This predictive equation can be used to estimate the biomass of trees for which only diameter was measured. The r^2 (a rough guide as to the predictive ability of the equation) is high (0.96). Review Chapter 7 if you have forgotten what r^2 represents. Now we can take the antilogarithm of −0.775

Figure 11.2

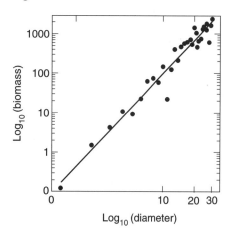

$(10^{-0.775} = 0.168)$ and estimate "a" in the original equation. We do not have to recalculate "b," because it is not transformed in either equation. Figure 11.3 shows the estimated position of the line with regard to the original data. The equation in terms of the untransformed data is:

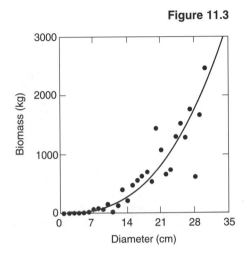

Figure 11.3

$$\text{Biomass} = 0.168 \times \text{Diameter}^{2.778}$$

We can see that the r^2 is meaningless with regard to the original data. The line does not explain about 96% of the variation in the data, and that variability changes along the line. The equation is very good at estimating the biomass of small trees, but large trees in the range of 27 to 30 cm diameter could have biomasses ranging from less than 1000 kg to more than 2000 kg.

Researchers sometimes present graphs of the transformed data, but the fit of the model can only be seen in relation to the original untransformed values.

Trial and Error Estimates without Transformation

The greater variability of the larger trees is real, and no model can make it disappear. However, the log transformation reduces the variability of the larger trees when the position of the line is estimated. This gives as much weight to a small tree as to a large tree when positioning the line. That was not what the biologist wanted. Slight errors in the estimation of biomass of small trees would have little effect on the estimate of forest biomass. However, even a slight change in the position of the line could change the estimate of the biomass of a single large tree by hundreds of kilograms.

The biologist looked for a method that would preserve the greater variability in the large trees, and therefore make them more important in the analysis. Linear models were not appropriate, so a computer-intensive nonlinear estimation technique was used. Even when the relationship cannot be linearized, reasonable estimates of the parameters can be obtained by trial and error (iterative) techniques.

The nonlinear models are partly trial and error, and partly mathematical. The program starts with arbitrary estimates of the parameters, applies the model

Figure 11.4

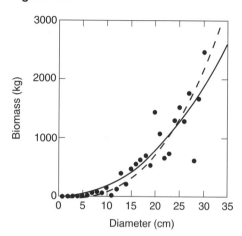

(equivalent to drawing the line), and calculates the deviations from the line. It then tries other values and sees whether they give smaller deviations of the observed data from the model. Mathematics are involved because the biologist has to give the general form of the equation, and because the computer uses mathematical algorithms to ensure that it generally moves the estimates in a direction that will minimize the deviations. These methods are very effective. The computer took 16 trials (called iterations) to estimate the following equation:

$$Biomass = 1.139 \times Diameter^{2.178}$$

The values of the parameters are slightly different than those estimated from the transformed data, but the curve whose parameters were estimated by iteration (the solid line in Figure 11.4) is positioned similarly to the curve whose parameters were estimated by linear transformation (the solid line in Figure 11.3, and dashed line in Figure 11.4).

The advantage for the biologist is that the nonlinear method better estimates the biomass of the large trees, even though it overestimates the biomass of the small trees. A model based on nonlinear regression is better for estimating the biomass of the forest, but is inappropriate for physiological questions about small trees. As always, there is no generally correct method, only methods more appropriate for specific questions.

Other Deviant Methods

Nonlinear models are also useful for estimating parameters when we do not want to use least-squares. Ordinary least-squares techniques are generally the best for prediction, but they may not describe relationships accurately. Consider the relationship between length and body height for a species of fish. For morphological data, a reduced major-axis (geometric-mean) regression might be the appropriate model (e.g., Ricker 1973).

It is easy to estimate the position of the reduced major-axis regression by instructing the program to use another equation (called the loss function) to minimize the area of the triangles formed between the points and the lines (see Chapter 7). Figure 11.5 shows the position of the line when we minimize squared deviations (solid line) and deviations for the reduced major-axis model (dashed line).

The difference is not very great, though it can be important in some cases, especially if the researcher analyzes the data in sections rather than over the whole range of the independent variable (Ricker 1973). The point is that any residual can be minimized by iteration, even if there is no simple mathematical formula for doing so.

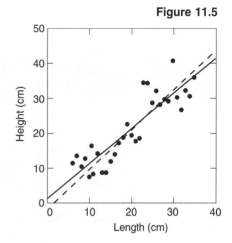

Figure 11.5

General Linear Models

In some cases, the assumptions of least-squares techniques are badly violated. The most common case is where the dependent variable is measured on a 0 or 1 scale (e.g., presence, absence; effect, no effect; died, survived). In that case, researchers use logistic regression to analyze the data. Most methods we used in this chapter are of the type referred to as general linear modeling (GLM). A model is specified and, if necessary, a transformation of the data carried out so that the model will be linear.

In GLM, the model on which the transformation is based is called the link function. To linearize the power function, we apply the same transformation to both sides of the equation, so the equality is maintained. However, not all transformations to obtain the appropriate link function have this property. Based on the expected form of the residuals, a deviance is minimized that is appropriate for the model and for the way the data are collected. It may be possible to do this algebraically, as with least-squares, but generally an iterative technique is used.

A method similar to GLM, called general additive modeling (GAM) is really just a GLM in which the curvilinear relationships are modeled by complex polynomials. It is sometimes called nonparametric, but it is only nonparametric in the sense that the form of the relationship is not assumed a priori (Guisan et al. 2002). GAMs have mainly been used for modeling species distributions along environmental gradients, a topic we will treat in more detail in Chapter 12. GAM may be better considered as being complementary to, rather than alternative to, GLM (Austin 2002).

Maximum Likelihood

The nonlinear techniques do not have to minimize residuals. Some authors use maximum-likelihood techniques. Maximum-likelihood techniques estimate parameters by choosing them to make the probability of the observed data as large as possible. Sokal and Rohlf (1995) state that, "The maximum-likelihood approach to fitting a regression line to bivariate or multivariate data is the general and correct method."

However, for small samples, the maximum-likelihood approach is neither unbiased nor efficient.

When the usual assumptions (plus a few others) for least squares regression are met, least squares regression gives the maximum-likelihood analyses. Mathematically minded readers might read Neyman (1937) to see how this and other techniques relate to probability theory. Friendly (1995) gives some useful physical analogies to maximum-likelihood estimation.

Moderate deviations from the assumptions do not result in large differences between least-squares and maximum-likelihood techniques. That is why few researchers bother to use maximum-likelihood. We do not know the real form of the distribution of residuals of biomass values used to construct Figure 11.1. However, assuming that it is strongly skewed to one side and can be modeled by a distribution called "Poisson"—which is frequently used in maximum-likelihood analyses—the maximum-likelihood estimates of the parameters result in the position of the solid line shown in Figure 11.6. This solid line almost completely overlaps the position of the broken line that is estimated by least-squares.

Maximum-likelihood methods minimize a likelihood function. However, the likelihood function can only be determined given a distribution of the residuals (Hilborn and Mangel 1997). Maximum-likelihood estimates can be calculated in a standard nonlinear (iterative) computer program by minimizing the negative of the log of the likelihood function. However, there are several different approaches to maximum-likelihood estimation (Bard 1974), and the results have different properties.

Once the model becomes moderately complex, there is no simple maximum-likelihood estimator and very complex procedures have to be programmed into the computer. It is virtually impossible to determine the form of the underlying distribution by inspecting the data. Therefore, maximum-likelihood methods are most appropriate when there are strong theoretical reasons for adopting a particular model (Guttman 1999) and when you have large samples. Do not consider using these techniques unless you can collaborate with a very competent statistician.

Figure 11.6

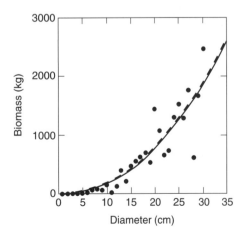

Most practitioners state that they use maximum-likelihood without giving the details of the methods and assumptions, so it is often hard for even experienced statisticians to evaluate the results. When reading the literature, you will usually have to interpret maximum-likelihood models as you would least-squares models, and hope that the author programmed the correct likelihood function for the model.

Pitfalls in Nonlinear Estimation

The nonlinear (iterative) techniques all have a weakness when used on complex models. The individual elements of the simple models can be described by straight or monotonically increasing or decreasing lines. However, complex models represent complex surfaces, which may have dimples in them (Figure 11.7). The iterative techniques generally approach the optimum solution, represented by the lowest point on the surface, in a series of jumps. The length of the jumps usually gets smaller with time, ensuring that the program does not keep jumping out of the best area. However, the estimation procedure may fall into a dimple (called a local minimum) instead of the lowest point (called the global minimum; see Figure 11.7).

To avoid basing conclusions on results that represent local minima, the researcher can start the process over again with the estimates obtained, or with different starting values, or make sure that the initial estimates are close to the most likely values. This introduces an element of subjectivity into the process that some researchers do not like. However, all modeling, even the statistical null-hypothesis modeling of conventional statistics, involves a great degree of subjectivity.

Complex models are hard to deal with, no matter what the method.

The concepts presented in this chapter have been complex, and we do not have the space to explore them in detail. However, they are statistical concepts, which are not as important as the general concepts presented in the previous chapters. In Chapter 10, we tried to find ways to make linear models more realistic when they had to reflect dependencies among independent variables. Many programs use maximum-likelihood methods to solve for the parameters of the linear equations in these models. Complex models can also be analyzed using nonlinear techniques, but usually no more satisfactorily.

Figure 11.7

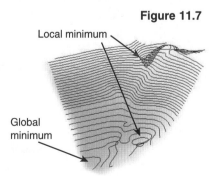

Local minimum

Global minimum

"Multivariate statistics is a huge field in which even experienced statisticians tread warily."

Multivariate Statistics: Cutting Down the Trees to Better See the Forest

Multivariate statistics have been likened to Pandora's box (James and McCulloch 1990). In Greek mythology, Pandora was a divine entity that carried all of mankind's evil in a box. Multivariate statistics is a huge field in which even experienced statisticians tread warily. Many of the multivariate and univariate techniques, including all that we have discussed so far, can be regarded as special cases of canonical correlation analysis (Harris 1975). However, we will concentrate on less mathematically demanding methods, and try to relate patterns observable on graphs to what the techniques are trying to reveal. In previous sections we covered relationships that could be dealt with mathematically or conceptually in terms of the following equation:

$$Y = a + b \times X_{\text{(possibly partial)}}$$

Most of the multivariate techniques used in ecology can be represented by the following conceptual equation:

$$Y_1, Y_2, Y_3, ... Y_i = a + b \times X_{\text{(possibly partial)}}$$

However, sometimes there are no independent variables. The objective of the analyses is to reduce the problem to something similar to the following equation:

$$Y' = a + b \times X_{\text{(possibly partial)}}$$

where Y' is a composite variable or variables thought to encompass the essence of the multiple dependent variables. The results can then be represented on a two- or three-dimensional graph.

Table 12.1							
Site	sp A	sp B	sp C	sp D	sp E	sp F	Rainfall (mm)
1	9	1	0	0	0	0	270
2	0	1	0	0	0	1	315
3	0	0	0	0	4	0	200
4	0	2	1	1	0	2	255
5	4	0	0	0	6	0	190
6	0	1	0	0	0	0	290
7	8	0	0	0	7	0	150
8	6	0	0	0	3	0	125
9	2	0	2	2	3	1	230
10	0	2	1	1	0	1	290
11	0	0	4	4	1	0	240
12	10	0	0	0	1	0	100

We start with ordination techniques because they deal with continuous variables and are useful for introducing the concepts that underlie most of the other techniques. Ordination techniques seek to order objects in some sensible manner without having to refer to all of the characteristics of each object. The simplest form is a direct ordination of the dependent variables on a single independent variable. Table 12.1 shows the data for a hypothetical study of the distribution of six plant species (SP_i) in relation to average rainfall at each site. The values for each species represent its density (number per 100 m^2) at each site. Species A and E are grasses, C and D are shrubs, and B and F are trees.

Graphs of Gradients

Figure 12.1A is a composite graph showing the distribution of each species against rainfall. We notice that the species do not have similar distributions along the rainfall gradient. Some have higher densities at sites with low rainfall, some have higher densities at sites with medium rainfall, and some have higher (but not very high) densities at sites with high rainfall. Rainfall does seem to be a factor influencing the species, but the individual relationships are not linear. The pattern would be clearer if we plotted the graphs in a different order, putting the species whose highest densities occur in high-rainfall areas in the upper graphs, and species whose highest densities occur in low-rainfall areas in the bottom graphs (Figure 12.1B).

Figure 12.1   (A)   (B)

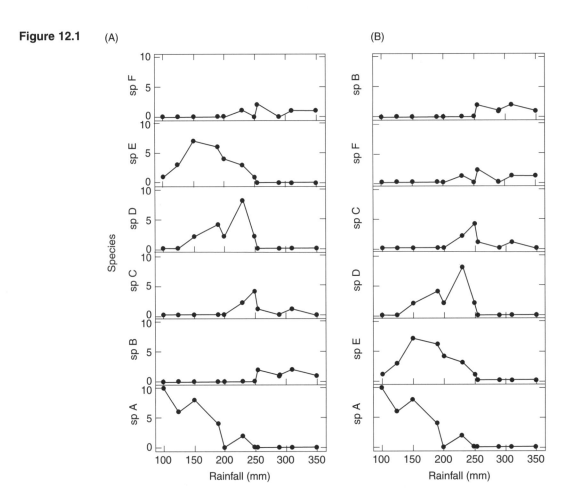

Figure 12.1 shows how rainfall sorts the species. The highest densities form a diagonal across the composite graph. This is called a direct-gradient analysis because we arranged the species in relation to a gradient that we expected to be important. Based on Figure 12.1B, we could say that individual species and the community in general, are organized along a rainfall dimension. Were we not able to produce a graph with the higher densities forming a diagonal, we would have to conclude that rainfall is not a strong determinant of community structure. Different types of structure may be reflected in different patterns on the graph.

However, we should never believe in a structure (pattern) unless it can be seen on a simple graph such as Figure 12.1B.

It seems strange that there are fewer plants in the high rainfall area, until we take into account the different life forms. You simply cannot stack as many trees into a small plot as you can grasses. We measured the community composition in terms of numbers of individuals, but this does not reflect the biomass, which is likely to be much greater for trees. One way to correct this imbalance would be to standardize the data by species. If we divide the number of individuals of each species found in each plot by the total number of that species, all of the species will be on an equivalent dimensionless scale that runs from 0 to 1 (Figure 12.2A).

The pattern is now clearer, with the trees having as much weight in our visual analysis as the grasses. However, this will not always be the case. Some species may be rare simply due to the vagaries of sampling, and giving undue weight to those species may obscure, rather than reveal, patterns. Instead of transforming

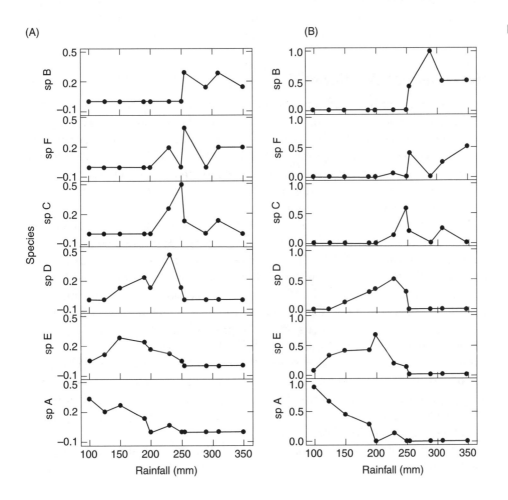

Figure 12.2

species, we could transform sites to have the same densities of individuals independent of species. In this case our visual analysis is not concerned with density per se; it emphasizes relative density (Figure 12.2B). However, be careful using proportions or other transformations that limit row totals since these can create spurious patterns in your data for some analyses (Jackson 1997).

Data transformations change biological interpretations (Noy-Meir et al. 1975, Pielou 1984, Johnson and Field 1993). In our example, the general pattern remains the same, but the details for each species changed. In fact, Figures 12.1B, 12.2A, and 12.2B answer different questions. Figure 12.1B is useful for questions about the relative species densities. Figure 12.2A is useful if we have questions about how the community would look if all species had equal abundance, and Figure 12.2B is useful for questions about relative abundance within, but not between plots. It is important to understand this before moving forward to the next section. Many of the most commonly used multivariate techniques have transformations of the original data built into them and the researcher must be sure that the transformation(s) is (are) appropriate for the question being asked.

Hypothetical Gradients

Our analysis so far has been concerned with an ecological gradient that we know exists. It asks whether some pattern related to the known gradient exists. However, there may be other, stronger patterns in the data that we miss because we concentrated on the rainfall gradient. Another way to approach the question is to ask whether there is a pattern in the data independent of any known gradients. For this, we must analyze the dependent variables without reference to any preconceived gradient. This is called indirect-gradient analysis.

There are many types of indirect-gradient analysis, but we start with one that does not require mathematics to understand the basics. It is called nonmetric multidimensional scaling (NMDS). The objective of this analysis is to describe the pattern shown by the six species in fewer dimensions than those presented in Table 12.1. One of the advantages of NMDS is that we can choose how many dimensions to look for. Since we know that there is a rainfall gradient, and we analyzed the data with regard to one dimension in the previous graphs, we will do a one-dimensional ordination of the sites with regard to species.

Ordering the sites requires an intermediate step. We have no information about the sites relative to an external gradient. We only have data on the relationships among sites based on the distribution of species. Therefore we ask how different sites are with regard to species. The question therefore arises as to what we regard as different. Different in relation to what species?

The simplest measure of overall difference (distance) is just to add the differences between sites with regard to each species. For instance, site 1 has nine individuals of species A, but site 2 has no individuals of species A. Therefore they differ by nine on that variable. Both sites have one individual of species B, so they differ by 0 for that species. The mean difference per species between site 1 and site 2, summing over all species, is $10/6 = 1.7$. If we carry out the same procedure for each pair of sites, we obtain Table 12.2, which is an association matrix.

Association matrices can have similarity or dissimilarity measures, and there are many different candidate measures. For instance, we could calculate the correlation between the values of species densities in each pair of sites which results in a similarity matrix of sites. Note, however, that the correlation coefficient implies a transformation that results in standardization by site. It is the equivalent to transforming values within sites to have a mean of 0 and standard deviation of one.

The distance we used, called Manhattan or city-block distance, is not the most commonly used measure of association or the one we recommend for this type of data. However, many of the better measures of associations are variations of it and it is useful for illustrating distances because it is intuitive and the calculations can be done on your fingers.

The values on the diagonal in Table 12.2 are all 0 because the distance between a site and itself is 0. We did not fill in the upper right part of the table because it would mirror the image of the lower portion. The table has all of the information about how far each site is from the others in terms of species composition. However, it has not simplified our problem much. In fact, this table has more cells than the original. We use NMDS to order the sites along a single axis such that, as far as possible, the distances of the sites along the axis are proportional to the dis-

Table 12.2

	# 1	# 2	# 3	# 4	# 5	# 6	# 7	# 8	# 9	# 10	# 11	# 12
# 1	0											
# 2	1.7	0										
# 3	2.7	1.3	0									
# 4	2.2	0.5	1.8	0								
# 5	2.7	2.7	1.3	3.2	0							
# 6	1.5	0.2	1.2	0.7	2.5	0						
# 7	1.8	3.2	1.8	3.7	1.2	3.0	0					
# 8	1.2	1.8	1.5	2.3	1.5	1.7	1.3	0				
# 9	3.7	2.7	2.0	2.8	2.0	2.8	3.2	2.5	0			
# 10	2.0	0.3	1.7	0.2	3.0	0.5	3.5	2.2	2.7	0		
# 11	2.8	1.5	1.2	1.7	2.5	1.3	3.0	2.3	2.2	1.5	0	
# 12	0.5	2.2	2.5	2.7	2.5	2.0	1.7	1.0	3.5	2.5	2.7	0

tances in Table 12.2. The program orders the sites by trial and error. It distributes the sites randomly along an axis like the *x*-axes in Figure 12.1. It then calculates the distances between sites along that axis and compares them to the distances in Table 12.2. The order of the distances among sites along the new axis is very different from the order of the distances in Table 12.2. However, the computer can use some tricky mathematics to reorder the sites on the next iteration to better approximate the order in the table. It keeps doing this until it cannot get closer to the original order by rearranging the points.

You could do the same process by hand, but it would take you much longer than the computer. Borg and Groenen (1997) give a very readable account of how the computer is programmed to do this. However, we just compare the computer order with our direct-gradient analysis because we are in the unusual situation of

Figure 12.3

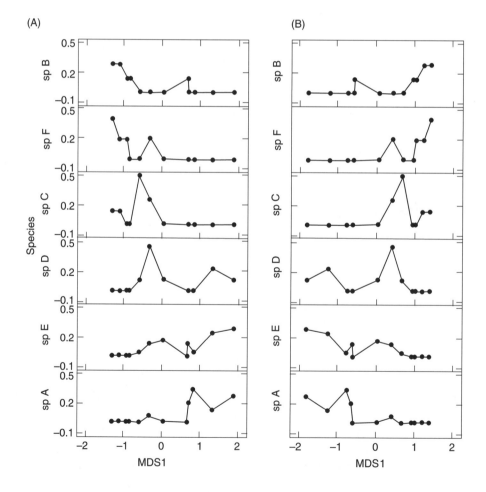

knowing what the real ecological gradient is. Figure 12.3A shows the sites along the new axis created by the NMDS program, which we call MDS1.

We notice that there is a diagonal pattern that runs in a direction opposite to that in Figure 12.2. The direction of the new axis is completely arbitrary because it was designed only to maintain the relative distances between the points. Therefore we can reverse the NMDS axis (Figure 12.3B).

The pattern is similar to that of rainfall, but the analysis has not been able to reproduce the original data exactly. MDS1 is a reasonable surrogate of rainfall, even though it ordered the sites without using any direct information about rainfall. It did this using only the similarities (more correctly, the dissimilarities) among sites in terms of plant densities. If we plot the true gradient (rainfall) against that predicted by the NMDS analysis (MDS1) (Figure 12.4), we find that the hypothetical axis predicts about 50% of the variation in rainfall.

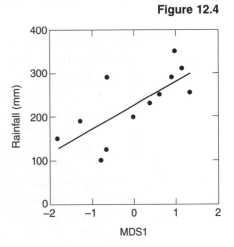

Figure 12.4

This result is pretty good, considering that the association of the original variables with rainfall is not unrealistically strong. None of the distributions of the species along the rainfall gradient (see Figure 12.1B) form a smooth curve, reflecting the type of variability expected for ecological data.

Indirect ordinations almost always follow the same steps, though this is not always obvious from the programs. First, the data may be transformed, and this depends on the question being asked. Then an association matrix of the distances (or similarities) between the objects is constructed. The association matrix is based on a measure that is averaged over all of the attributes. Therefore there is only one distance between each pair of objects that is analyzed by the program, independent of how many variables (attributes) were measured.

The program then arranges the objects along one or more (usually more) axes (dimensions) that best reflect the patterns that are in the data. Hopefully, those axes reflect ecological variables that caused the pattern in the data. At best, we expect only a rough approximation of the real underlying dimensions and, if we choose an inappropriate transformation, association measure, or ordination technique, there may be no correspondence between the derived axes and the real ecological gradients (see Kenckel and Orloci 1986, and McCune and Grace 2002 for examples).

Sometimes the researcher is interested in an ordination of the attributes (species in our example) rather than objects (sites in our example), and some methods can do simultaneous ordinations of the objects and attributes. However, the same logic applies.

More Than One Dimension

We could ask the NMDS program to arrange the sites in two dimensions (Figure 12.5). We know that there is only one meaningful gradient in these data because we created them. However, we can still see the pattern in two dimensions. By making the size of the symbols proportional to rainfall (Figure 12.5A) or labeling the below-average rainfall sites "L" and the above-average rainfall sites "H" (Figure 12.5B), we can see the association between rainfall and the similarity of the sites in terms of species composition. Had we included too many axes we would have degraded the pattern.

There is a great deal of literature on selection of the number of axes to include, especially for eigenvector analyses, which we will describe in the next section (Jackson 1993). However, it is rare that a pattern is discernable in more than two dimensions, and analyzing too many dimensions defeats the purpose of the exercise, which is to reduce dimensionality (Gauch 1982a, James and McCulloch 1990). Often, axes that are not "significant" on internal criteria may be meaningfully related to external gradients (Gauch 1982b, Økland 1999).

> There are many ways of doing multidimensional scaling (MDS), and these may be nonmetric, metric, or a hybrid between the two (see Borg and Groenen 1997 page 199; Faith, Minchin and Belbin 1987).

It is often said that the MDS axes do not have a logical interpretation. It is true that we can rotate the axes to any position in the plane of data without changing the relative distances between the points. The program we used rotates the axes to

Figure 12.5

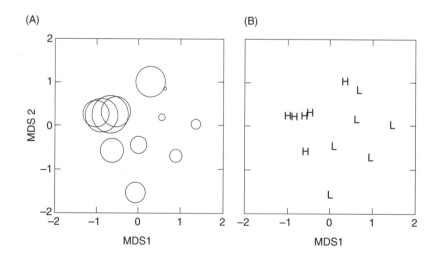

give the maximum correlation between the original variables and the first MDS axis. However, that does not necessarily make sense, as the distances between the points are not derived from correlations. The rainfall gradient appears to run as a diagonal across the two-dimensional MDS representation. There is another class of ordination techniques, based on eigenvector analyses, in which the derived axes can be related mathematically to the original variables.

Eigenvector Analyses

Given some important, and often improbable assumptions, the position of the "phantom axes" in multivariate space can be determined by matrix algebra (eigenvector analyses) instead of trial and error. Analyses based on this principal are called *"eigen"* analyses, or eigenvector analyses. *"Eigen"* is a German word meaning "characteristic." Eigenvectors are multivariate axes derived directly from the attributes (characteristics) of the objects.

The first eigenvector-based ordination technique to be widely used was principal components analysis (PCA), which generally uses the Pearson correlation coefficient as its measure of association (Pearson 1901). Other techniques are variations on it. For instance, correspondence analysis (CA) can be calculated in the same way as PCA, after substituting the Chi-square distance for the correlation coefficient and range-standardizing objects. If some other distance is used, and the association matrix is transformed to give it metric properties, the analysis is called principal coordinates analysis (PCoA).

PCA and CA are popular because they are easy to calculate, the derived axes can be related mathematically to the original variables, and it is possible to project the objects and attributes onto the same coordinate space. However, some of their advantages are illusory. They assume linear relationships among the variables that may not exist. PCA is especially sensitive to this assumption and, if the sites are range-standardized before the analysis is undertaken, the PCA axes are artifactual (Jackson 1977). The distributions of species along ecological gradients frequently do not conform to the models that underlie the most commonly used ordination techniques (Austin 2002, McCune and Grace 2002, Oksanen and Minchin 2002).

For long gradients, in which most attributes do not have non-negative values along most of the gradient, eigen analyses (and NMDS analyses) tend to distort the relationships among objects and give horseshoe shapes to linear gradients. A variant of CA, de-trended correspondence analysis (DCA), purports to straighten these "arch" effects, but it is as likely to straighten relationships that were truly curvilinear in ecological space (see Wartenberg et al. 1987).

Kenckel and Orlocci (1986) and McCune and Grace (2002) give sobering examples of what DCA can do to known gradients. Also, DECORANA, the program that made CA and DCA so popular, and which was used by most authors who published on the technique, had a bug (Oksanen and Minchin 1997).

This is worrying, and illustrates why it is important to critically analyze the results of multivariate analyses in relation to the original data before putting too much faith in them.

For analyses in a single plane (two dimensions), De'ath (1999) has shown that smoothing with a technique called principal curves analysis beyond what can be achieved by the ordination techniques, can better recover ecological gradients. However, that is far beyond the scope of this introductory text.

The apparent relationship between the original variables and the derived axes is rarely simple for any analysis. The apparent geometric relationships are real only if you use a geometric measure such as euclidean distance, you have not transformed the variables, and if all the variables are truly measurable on the same scale. If you use environmental variables such as pH, temperature, conductivity, water velocity, and sediment thickness, it is ridiculous to think that these attributes can be combined geometrically in any meaningful sense. Even plant densities are not comparable unless the species have similar life forms and sizes. Combining numbers of liverworts, grasses, shrubs, and trees is just as esoteric as combining temperature and water velocity.

Despite the different methodological and conceptual bases, the pattern captured by the MDS ordination (see Figure 12.5) and the first two axes of the PCA (Figure 12.6) are similar.

If the pattern in the data is very strong, and caused by only a few underlying gradients, all of the commonly used methods will yield similar conclusions. However, the differences in these conclusions can be important. We would not recommend the analyses presented above for the data in Table 12.1. Other association measures and (or) transformations are appropriate for most ecological studies (Legendre and Legendre 1998, Legendre and Gallagher 2001). We use standardization by division by row totals and city-block distances only as a simplified introduction to the techniques.

The only way to determine the best method is to consider the pattern that the underlying gradient is likely to create in the data (e.g., Kenckel and Orloci 1986). If you cannot draw a hypothetical graph or table that illustrates the patterns that might be in the data, do not proceed to the next step of looking for those patterns. Gauch published a very clear book on multivariate techniques in 1982. Most of his discussion of the appropriate ordination techniques is outdated and his recommendations differ from many that we make here. However, his discussion of the uses of multivariate techniques and the patterns in data tables are as current as

Figure 12.6

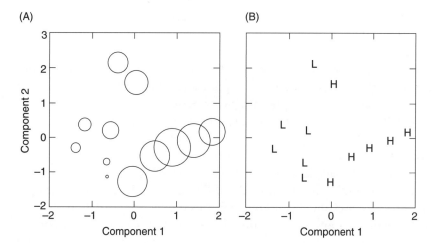

they were 20 years ago. His introductory chapter is still one of the best overviews of multivariate techniques in ecology and could form the basis of any introductory course in multivariate techniques for ecologists.

There is no all-purpose technique. For instance, Azevedo-Ramos et al. (1999) used MDS and the Bray-Curtis association measure to ordinate a tadpole community. In the same paper, they used MDS with the Gower association measure to ordinate predator communities, and PCA to ordinate environmental variables. Each one was chosen to reflect a different type of pattern. However, we cannot go into the details of those techniques here without losing sight of the overall concepts, which we need to understand before considering other multivariate methods.

Deep Culture: Significance Tests

Now that you have some idea of what underlying dimensions (we believe that "phantom axes" is a more descriptive term) are in relation to data, we can return to some direct-ordination techniques that are usually employed only to evaluate the "significance" of known gradients. The most general is a multivariate analysis that is analogous to multiple regression, which we call "redundancy analysis" (RDA). Unfortunately, Markarenkov and Legendre (2002) used the same term (redundancy analysis) for a much more restricted analysis that we call canonical redundancy analysis (CRDA). Consider the following equation:

$$Y_1, Y_2, Y_3 ... Y_i = a + b_1 \times X_1 + b_2 \times X_2 + ... b_i \times X_i$$

The analysis asks if there is a linear combination of the variables on the left-hand side of the equation that can be explained by linear combinations of the variables on the right-hand side. Note our emphasis on *linear*. If the structure in the data on the left-hand side could not be captured by PCA you should not be using these techniques.

There are many multivariate test statistics and each has different assumptions. In any case, the interpretation of a "significant" result is not easy, as it may have come about because of a single variable or a combination of variables. If you find that something is "significant," you still need to do a lot of exploring to find out what happened. That is probably why it is rare to find examples of RDA in the ecological literature.

In terms of our data, in which we have only one explanatory variable, the three most common multivariate statistics (Wilks' lambda, Pillai trace, and Hotelling-Lawley trace) reject the null hypothesis of no effect of rainfall at $P = 0.070$. We asked whether rainfall explains any of the variation in the dependent variables. However, a different but equally valid question would be, "Does rainfall explain the major pattern in the dependent variables?" We know that there is only one underlying gradient in these data, but you would not know this in a field situation. Assuming that the two MDS axes are the best representation of the major pattern in the dependent variables, we can do an RDA on the two MDS variables. This rejects the null hypothesis of no effect of rainfall at $P = 0.023$.

Both questions are valid, but the difference is important. The second question, which only asks about the effect of rainfall on the *major* pattern, is the most powerful. This is generally true. By using the indirect ordination to reduce dimensionality, we are able to focus on the patterns instead of the total variability and are better able to identify an effect. This is not because MDS is better able to handle nonlinear relationships than the eigen analyses, or because RDA analyses should not be applied to MDS axes (Anderson and Willis 2003). RDA of the first two PCA axes rejects the hypothesis of no effect of rainfall at $P = 0.027$. Gauch (1982a,b) called this process "noise reduction by eigenvector ordinations," but our non-eigenvector ordination is also effective.

Remember, also, that the unexplained variability may be the result of trying to fit the data into an inappropriate model rather than the result of random "noise" (Økland 1999).

Hopefully, you have been wondering why we categorized a continuous variable in Figures 12.5B and 12.6B. We certainly do not generally recommend this, though it is sometimes useful to convey a pattern quickly in three-dimensional graphs such as Figures 12.5 and 12.6, especially in seminars. For the purpose of illustration, we will now assume that the low and high rainfall categories are truly categorical and apply the multivariate analog of ANOVA using these categories.

All the caveats given for the univariate case apply to multivariate analysis of variance (MANOVA). It is really just a special case of multivariate multiple regression (or RDA), which uses dummy variables to code the categories. There are many statistics that can be used to evaluate the significance of MANOVA, but simulations indicate that the Pillai trace is the most least affected by violations of assumptions (Olson 1976, Johnson and Field 1993). A nonparametric analogue of MANOVA that uses randomization to generate probability values (Anderson 2001) may be more appropriate in some situations.

Applying MANOVA, we can reject the null hypothesis of no effect of rainfall categories on linear combinations of the dependent variables at $P = 0.021$. Again, if we had asked only about the major patterns, and used MANOVA to test for an effect of the rainfall categories on the MDS axes (Johnson and Field 1993), we would have had a more powerful test and rejected the null hypothesis at $P = 0.002$.

Association Matrix (Mantel) Analyses

There are a number of tests for effects of continuous or categorical variables that operate directly on the association matrix (see Table 12.2 for an example of our association matrix). These are derived from the Mantel test (Mantel and Varland 1970), which is a permutation test similar in principle to the DIF test discussed in Chapter 5. They use more information than is in the ordination axes, and when there is only one gradient being tested they may be more powerful for detecting known gradients.

Permutation tests for the effect of rainfall as a continuous variable, or as two categories reject the null hypothesis of no effect of rainfall at $P < 0.001$ and $P = 0.006$, respectively. However, when there are more than two categories (e.g., Luo and Fox 1996), or more than one independent variable is investigated (Anderson and Legendre 1999) they are sometimes less powerful than analyses of the major patterns derived by indirect ordination. Note that the technique recommended by Smouse et al. (1986) probably has an unacceptably high Type I error rate (Anderson and Legendre 1999).

As with other direct-gradient analyses, Mantel tests ask whether there is some association, not whether the factors account for the major patterns. They also have a deficiency because they generally only test for a pattern in the data that is associated with the dependent variable(s), and do not describe that pattern. However, extensions of the concept to detect spatial patterns may be very useful (e.g., Fortin and Gurevitch 1993, Legendre 1993, Sawada 1999). They can be powerful tests to detect spatial pseudoreplication. As with other statistical techniques, they are of limited use in refining our biological models if we only use them to generate probability values. They test the hypothesis but give no real indication as to why it is or is not rejected.

Peres-Neto and Jackson (2001) describe a test based on Procrustes superimposition, which potentially uses all of the original distances and is more powerful than the Mantel test previously described. However, Peres-Neto and Jackson (2001) used the technique after reducing dimensionality by ordination. In this case, only the major patterns recorded by the ordination are investigated, and the technique gives similar results to some of the procedures described in the next section.

Canonical Analyses

An apparently attractive eigenvector method of direct-gradient analysis is canonical correspondence analysis (CCA), which plots objects, attributes, and the predictor variables all in the same graph (ter Braak 1986). It appears to do everything you might want. However, there are two different ways to use this analysis (McCune 1997). If you use it as a direct-gradient analysis, it will ignore major patterns not associated with the expected gradients that would have been found by indirect-gradient analysis (Økland 1996). If you use it in its original form, it is really just an indirect-gradient analysis followed by tests of association of the independent ("environmental") variables with the derived gradients (McCune 1997).

> **Few researchers understand the difference between tests based on direct vs. indirect gradient analyses.**

Legendre and Legendre (1988) explain the steps necessary to obtain the ordination for CCA, but the matrix algebra involved is beyond the programming capacity of most biologists. The logic of CCA is better understood after becoming familiar with a closely related technique, Legendre's and Legendre's (1998) redundancy analysis.

The analysis described by Legendre and Legendre (1998) is more complicated than the redundancy analysis (RDA) we described earlier in this chapter, and the name canonical redundancy analysis (CRDA) is probably more appropriate. We used RDA to analyze the results of an indirect gradient. Legendre and Legendre (1998) used multiple regression to model the linear relationships between the independent variables and each dependent variable separately. The values predicted by the regressions are substituted for the original data, and an ordination is undertaken using the predicted values. This guarantees linear relationships between the attributes and the independent variables, but the resulting ordination axes may have little relationship to the original variables.

CRDA has the assumption that there are linear relationships between the dependent and independent variables, and CCA assumes that it is possible to derive such relationships through matrix manipulation. To overcome this restriction, Makarenkov and Legendre (2002) developed nonlinear CRDA and CCA based on polynomial regression. This is a multivariate extension of GAM (Guisan et al. 2002), and the assumptions of the analyses are more realistic than for linear CCA and CRDA. However, the interpretation of the results is more complicated, with two (and potentially more) vectors for each predictor variable.

Legendre and Anderson (1999) transformed nonmetric distance measures to make them metric and then used redundancy analysis in a factorial design to relate independent variables to PCoA axes. Redundancy analysis is a method of deriving unique variance, and is similar in principle to the variance allocation techniques that we have considered in previous chapters. Legendre and Anderson then evaluated the significance of the statistics with permutation tests.

This approach allows for testing interactions in an experimental situation, and is similar in principle to the use of PCA to produce linear additive variables for regression analysis (e.g., Short et al. 1983), except that the ordination of the dependent variables is constrained by the independent variables. Although the analysis produces one less PCoA axis than the number of objects, regardless of the number of attributes, it is not used primarily to reduce dimensionality. Rather it can be considered a transformation to produce variables that meet the assumptions of the variance allocation analysis. Legendre and Anderson (1999) give examples that illustrate how this technique allows for interpretations of interactions as well as the main effects that were observed in an indirect-gradient (MDS) analysis.

Legendre and Gallagher (2001) show how transformations of the original data allow many distance measures to be represented by Euclidean distances, considerably extending the possibilities for PCA and redundancy analyses.

Méot et al. (1998) explain even more complicated mathematics that separate the effects of spatial and environmental variation. However, extreme care is needed when phantom variables are substituted for real variables (Johnson and Field 1993). It may be very difficult to determine what really changed. Remember that another data set collected from the same system will generate different axes, no matter what the technique. If you are blessed with many independent observations, you can divide your data into exploration and validation subsets (e.g., Hallgren et al. 1999).

More recently, researchers have attempted to partition variance directly from the distance matrix itself, with no corrections and no eigen analysis (McArdle and Anderson 2001), or to partition the variance in the original variables space (Anderson 2001). These subjects are much too complex to be treated here.

Free programs for most of the analyses described in this chapter are available from Pierre Legendre's website, and the textbook by Legendre and Legendre (1998) is required reading for anyone considering multivariate analyses. The theory and practice for most of the techniques described in previous chapters have been well established for over 50 years. However, you will note that most of the references in this section were published within the last five years. Practice has far outstripped theory and experience in multivariate analyses.

> **Therefore, you should be very careful when using multivariate techniques, otherwise you may just be substituting weak inferences about strong variables with strong inferences about weak variables.**

Interpretation of these analyses is an art. If you are not feeling very artistic after reading the preceding section, you probably should not use multivariate techniques.

Discriminating between Groups

Another technique that tests for direct gradients is discriminant function analysis (DFA). This method is closely related to MANOVA, and tries to determine the linear combinations of variables that best discriminate between two or more groups. It has all of the usual assumptions (Williams 1983), and most published ecological studies that use DFA have had inadequate sample sizes (Williams and Titus 1988). DFA can be used to produce graphs that look like the plots obtained with indirect ordination. However, these plots have a very different interpretation (Manly 1997). We illustrate this by applying discriminant function analysis to try to separate the high (> 260 mm), medium (191 – 260 mm), and low (< 190 mm) rainfall sites in Table 12.1 based on vegetation (Figure 12.7A).

The separation of the low (L) medium (M) and high (H) sites in Figure 12.7A appears reasonable, and the program informs us that it correctly classified all of the sites. However, this graph is not equivalent to indirect ordinations in which the independent variable was not used to position the sites. Figure 12.7B shows the same DFA analysis that was used to generate Figure 12.7A, but the species data were substituted with data produced by a random-number generator. The separation looks even better, and the program correctly classifies all of the sites in relation to the rainfall categories. Interpretation of the graphs produced by CCA and CRDA suffer from the same problems as interpretation of graphs produced by DFA.

All of these analyses are based on direct-gradient analyses in which the patterns were forced to maximally coincide with the predictor variables. DFA will always find linear combinations of the variables that separate the categories, especially if there are a small number of replicates as is typical of ecological studies (Williams and Titus 1988). Do not place any confidence in equations to separate categories that have been generated by DFA unless they have been validated on an independent data set, or at least by a randomization procedure, such as the

(A)

(B)

Figure 12.7

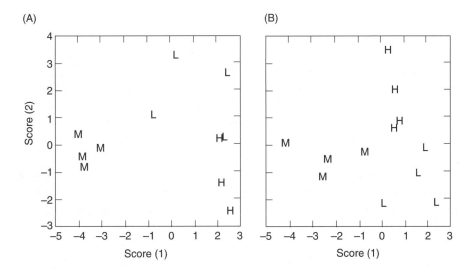

jackknife (Manel et al. 1999). Manly (1997) describes how to use the jackknife and other randomization tests.

> It is important to understand that there is a great conceptual divide between graphs produced by indirect-gradient analyses and graphs produced by direct-gradient analyses.

In Chapter 5 we showed that statistical tests are basically a simplified form of comparing a graph of observed results to a large number of graphs of the results expected when the null hypothesis is correct. Therefore, almost all graphs in this book involve observed results or results expected when the null hypothesis is true. In contrast, the graphs produced by the direct gradient analyses (DFA, CCA, and CRDA) show a result expected if the null hypothesis is false. It is not possible to evaluate the likelihood that the null hypothesis is false based on these graphs. To evaluate the null hypothesis, you must consult the associated statistical tests. You should not use these graphs unless you are confident that you, and your readers, understand the difference.

Categories that Grow on Trees

The association among objects is similar to the branching of a tree, in which close leaves unite to form a bunch, close bunches unite to form a branch, and branches unite to form the trunk of the tree. The most common examples relate to phylogenetic relationships. Most modern hypotheses about phylogenetic relationships are based on cladistic analyses, and these are far from simple. The attributes are sorted logically or statistically so that distances among taxa are based only on what are believed to be shared derived characteristics (synapomorphies). Many systematists do not believe that species should be grouped into arbitrary clusters, but this is exactly what is done in classical systematics, in which higher taxa, such as genera and families, are considered to represent clusters of species.

If you found the concept of association matrices and the various potential measures of ecological distance complicated, then it is going to take a while for you to get your head around cladistic analyses. You may, however, be forced to become conversant with this literature if you have a problem with phylogenetic pseudoreplication (see Chapter 5). We will consider only tree diagrams (dendrograms) that are based on simple ecological distances such as those used in the ordination analyses.

Trees can be constructed in the form of a dichotomous key (e.g., regression trees). However, most of the analyses use an association matrix, such as Table 12.2, to determine the distances between objects, and between nodes of the tree. The process can be agglomerative, adding objects one at a time to form groups, or divisive, separating the species hierarchically into subsets until each subset consists of only one object.

Groups can be defined by the distance to the center of the group, the distance to the closest member, the distance to the furthest member, and in a number of other ways. Again, we are looking for patterns in the data matrix, and there is no point in looking for such patterns unless you can imagine what they might look like in a hypothetical data matrix.

The choice of a cluster technique is probably more difficult than the choice of an ordination technique, and the decision as to which to use should be made based on the expected structure in the data. Using all possible combinations of transformations, distance measures and clustering techniques can just about guarantee to produce one cluster that conforms to your a priori ecological hypothesis. However, this is a trivial use of statistics.

Some researchers recommend that cluster techniques be used together with ordination techniques for preliminary data analysis (e.g., Gauch 1982a, Belbin 1992). This is appropriate if you intend to allow the computer to generate hypotheses for you, but it is rarely efficient. The trees generated by cluster analyses appear to be in two dimensions, but this is illusory. They represent mobiles that can be rotated through any angle at each node. They appeal to us because they appear to categorize the world, and humans feel more comfortable with categories than realistic continuous variables (see Chapter 7).

Ordination analyses can reveal clusters because clusters are formed by abrupt gradients. However, cluster analyses are often inefficient at revealing smooth gradients. In addition, they only seek clusters represented by certain shapes in the multivariate space. We illustrate this with data on measurements of students from a recent statistics class. The variables measured were diameters of the head, neck, chest, waist and thigh, and leg length.

Cluster analyses are indirect-gradient analyses, but we can only evaluate them if we use data with known gradients. Experience tells us that the categories "men" and "women" differ in shape, so we will use ordination and cluster analysis to see whether we can identify that difference. The cluster analysis mixes the five women among the men (Figure 12.8). The women tend to be considered very different from each other (long distances along the branches) and they are in five different major clusters. Based on this analysis, we are unlikely to retain the hypothesis that sex affects human form.

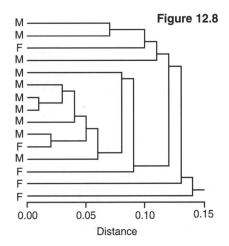

Figure 12.8

Before clustering, we carried out a transformation to row-standardize the data (standardized objects are equal to persons with the same overall size in this example) because we were interested in seeing whether the analysis could detect differences in form between the men and women. Had we not standardized the data, differences may have been due simply to size. As with all multivariate techniques, transformations of the data change the question that is being asked. Using the same transformation and distance measure, a two-dimensional MDS analysis produces a pattern that clearly indicates that men and women generally differ in form, even though some individuals are closer to members of the opposite sex than they are to the members of their own sex (Figure 12.9).

The gradient analysis (continuous variables) can detect the pattern better than the analysis that was trying to create categories, even though the pattern we were looking for could grossly be described by categories. All of the commonly used distance measures and clustering and ordination techniques give qualitatively similar results for this example. The fact that the categorical variable "sex" cannot explain much of the detail hopefully leads us to look for continuous variables such as hormone level or age that might be better predictors.

In order to determine the number of meaningful clusters in a data set, you have to know a lot about the structure of the data (Milligan and Cooper 1985, Dale 1988). If you decide that you can predict the form of your clusters a priori, and therefore

Figure 12.9

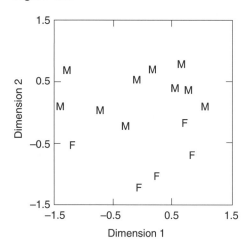

can select an appropriate clustering algorithm, you can use a technique called "bootstrapping," (which is one of the randomization techniques; Manly 1997) to help identify the number of natural clusters (Pillar 1999).

If you want to simultaneously decide on the "best" number of clusters and estimate the parameters that describe those clusters, consider the use of minimum message length (MML) clustering, an information theory technique that shows considerable promise (Wallace and Dowe 2000). However, MML techniques are at the forefront of computer science, and they are unlikely to be found in standard statistical packages in the near future. You can combine statistical tests with multivariate cluster analyses in "regression trees" (De'ath 2002). Regression-tree analysis is available in several commercial statistical packages. Regression trees can be used to analyze the effects of variables that are not independent, and for which you cannot assume simple linear models. However, the resulting categories may be difficult to interpret and may result from other confounding variables not included in the model. This is not an analysis for beginners, and simpler techniques, such as the ordinations presented in this book, should be tried before venturing into multivariate clustering. The number of potential analyses is enormous, and the selection of an appropriate cluster technique can only be made with a profound understanding of the processes that cause the patterns in a given data set.

Selecting Variables

Multivariate analyses share the difficulty of selecting variables with the simpler analyses. However, the principles are different. Students often use the same criteria suggested for multiple regression analyses to select variables. They often exclude dependent variables that are highly correlated with others. This is totally illogical. Remember that the analyses are looking for associations that repeat among variables. Gauch (1982a) called these associations coordinated variation.

Variables that carry the same information are in some sense redundant (hence the term "redundancy analysis" for some multivariate techniques). It is these associations that form the patterns in the data. If you select variables so as to reduce associations, you will take the major patterns out of the data, and your analysis will be restricted to examining the lesser patterns.

Conversely, you can create any pattern you like by judicious choice of variables. Often, many variables represent the same thing, or they may be the same variable measured in a different way. This problem is called aliasing (Mac Nally 1994). Depending on the associations among the aliases, aliasing may mask or enhance patterns. For example, consider the major patterns in stream characteristics: if factors like calcium concentration, pH, conductivity, and stream depth comprise the major patterns and therefore the most important dimension (component, axis, or phantom variable) then this dimension will most likely be associated with stream chemistry. By including a large number of variables that represent stream size such as width, cross-sectional area, discharge, distance from the sea, and macrophyte cover, the most important dimension (component, axis, or phantom variable) will now be related to physical variables.

If you think about patterns as representing associations in the original data matrix, you will soon see that it is possible to generate any pattern you want by selecting the right combination of variables. Variable selection must be made on criteria that are independent of any potential external variables that will be screened; otherwise the inferences are meaningless.

Multivariate Indices that Masquerade as Univariate Variables

Many ecological indices can be treated mathematically as though they were univariate. However, they are essentially multivariate (composed of a number of dependent variables), and their interpretation is as complicated as any of the multivariate statistics.

Examples include biomass, species richness, species diversity, and productivity. These are all generated by a number of other variables, and considering them as meaningful units can lead to illogical conclusions. Pélissier et al. (2003) show how many species diversity indices can be derived from species association matrices.

Even simple counts of species may confound species richness and evenness (Thompson and Withers 2003). Consider two sites with identical mammal species richness. One has only species of introduced murid rodents, whereas the other has rodents, ungulates, carnivores, and proboscideans. Few lay persons consider these sites equally diverse. Alternatively, the objective of a study could be to increase species diversity of mammals in a reserve. The reserve has 100 tapirs, 100 peccaries, 50 agoutis, 50 capybaras, 50 pacas, and a pair of jaguars. The jaguars reduce the density of agoutis, capybaras, and pacas more than the densities of the more difficult prey, the tapirs and peccaries. Without the jaguars, there would be 60 agoutis, 60 pacas, and 60 capybaras.

In the absence of the jaguars, the densities of peccaries and tapirs is reduced to 85 each, either in absolute terms (via competition) or statistically (because their relative densities decrease with an increase in the other prey even if their absolute densities remain constant). It is therefore obvious that the most economical way to increase the biodiversity of the reserve is to shoot the jaguars. The original reserve (Shannon's H = 1.58) lost one species and two individuals from the total but becomes marginally more diverse (Shannon's H = 1.59) because the evenness of the remaining species increases.

That is hardly what most people have in mind when they are talking about increasing diversity. Be wary of simple interpretations of multivariate statistics even when they masquerade as univariate measures (Feinsinger 2001, Magnusson 2002). Just as with the other multivariate statistics, you must be sure of what they represent in terms of the original variables in order to use them wisely.

Know What You Are Looking for before You Start

This ends our brief and superficial tour of multivariate techniques. The graphs, diagrams, and probability values associated with multivariate analyses are very easy to generate in modern computer programs. However, we hope that this brief overview has shown you that interpretation of these results is very difficult, and very dependent on decisions made while examining graphs or tables of the original data. Sometimes you can answer the questions just by looking at the tables if they are organized properly (Ehrenberg 1981).

The question of whether external variables cause any pattern, or cause the major pattern in the data is very important (Økland 1996). Researchers seem to understand this for univariate questions. For instance, everyone recognizes the difference between the following two statements: (1) Predators cause populations of microtine rodents to show cyclical patterns. This says that predators cause the major pattern. (2) Predators have some effect on the pattern of population fluctuations in microtine rodents. This says that predators cause some pattern that is not necessarily the most conspicuous one. However, few researchers seem to understand the difference in multivariate analyses.

Many texts suggest that multivariate analyses should be used for generating, rather than, testing hypotheses; however, it is not. If you need the computer to generate hypotheses for you, you should not be a scientist. One sort of question requires indirect-gradient analyses to detect the major patterns before you make the test. It can be considered a form of multivariate smoothing (De'ath 1999). The other sort of question involves direct-gradient analyses and is not concerned with whether the patterns are the major ones in the data or not (Økland 1996).

Many multivariate questions can be resolved with simple scatterplot matrices (Basford and Tukey 1999). Before you apply the more complicated techniques, make sure that you can create your own hypothetical gradients. Start with a program such as COMPAS (Minchin 1987) to make sure that you understand the basic factors that create (or hide) patterns in the data.

By simply rearranging the order of attributes and objects in the data table, meaningful inferences can often be made without using complicated techniques (Braun-Blanquet 1932, Gauch 1982a). Try out the techniques on simulated data to make sure that they do detect the patterns you are interested in. If you find constructing gradients too hard because you do not know what they are, then you are not prepared to go looking for something that you will not know how to recognize. Most "specialists" in multivariate analyses are really just specialists in the use of a particular computer program. The art in using multivariate analyses lies in choosing the appropriate options to detect the patterns expected to be in your data, and the best options might not be in the program that is in your computer. We recommend that readers exercise caution, and take the time to learn the limitations of these analyses before trying to explore all of their great potential. Passing this test of time, you will be apt to make use of Pandora's divine gifts, without being contaminated by the contents of her box.

## CHAPTER 13

"Writing up the study is the hardest part."

How to Write Better Backwards

Many students spend most of their time worrying about statistical tests, but writing up the study is the hardest part. Of course it is easier if the researcher knows from the start that data collection and statistical treatments are part of the communication process, and that mistakes made early in the study impede written or oral communication at the end. However, we have seen that there are powerful cultural forces working within science that induce us to collect data that are worthless for anything other than cultural identification. It is only when we try to communicate the results to other people, especially when we try to communicate with people who are not part of the scientific culture, that we discover how successful we have been at collecting and analyzing data.

Writing is not easy, and it usually does not get much easier with experience. Competent researchers do not keep repeating the same study, each time doing it better. After dominating one aspect, they move on to investigate and communicate about more complex phenomena. The communication difficulties increase with each new study, especially if the researcher finds it necessary to use complex statistical manipulations that few readers are familiar with. Basically, our flow charts get more complicated as we learn more.

Nevertheless, there are some simple rules that we can use to keep ourselves on track. Magnusson (1996) called this process "how to write backwards." Scientific questions can generally be divided into two groups based on complexity. "How" and "what" questions are usually simple, and are often associated with the trivial uses of statistics described in the early part of this book. "Why" questions are usually more complicated, and most of the debate in the literature is about the appropriate null hypotheses for "why" questions (see Connor and Simberloff 1986).

A Simple Conceptual Scheme

We start our discussion with a simple "how" question as this facilitates communication. However, "how" and "what" questions usually do not interest many people unless the answer is a very unexpected one. For instance, for centuries nobody bothered to ask, "How do baby crocodiles get from the egg buried in the nest to the safety of water?" When Tony Pooley showed that the mother digs up the eggs, breaks open the eggshells, carries the babies in her mouth, and releases them into the water, everyone thought the question very interesting. We will illustrate the basic "backwards" writing technique with a "how" question, and briefly discuss some of the difficulties of "why" questions at the end of this chapter.

The first step in the process is to write down what the major conclusions of your study are. These should be simple and without modifiers. For instance, we might have concluded that, "The quantity of ants in the diet of some frogs is related to the intensity of their foraging activity." Keeping in mind that relationships may be hidden, or even distorted by confounding variables, we need to see if we can produce a two-dimensional graph that illustrates the way in which the amount of ants in the diet varies with the intensity of foraging, without confounding patterns introduced by other variables. The amount of ants in the diet of frogs varies seasonally and with the size of the frog, but for simplicity we assume that the researcher used the appropriate statistical techniques to isolate the effect of foraging activity from the effects of season and size, and is able to produce a partial plot in two dimensions that illustrates the conclusion (Figure 13.1).

To evaluate whether the graph supports the conclusion, we first have to make sure that the dimensions of the graph reflect the dimensions in the conclusion. Our conclusion is that the amount of ants varies with intensity of foraging. Therefore, the y-axis (dependent variable) has to represent "number of ants," and the x-axis (independent variable) has to represent "intensity of foraging." There is no other choice.

As the axes must represent these dimensions, and only these dimensions, useful graphs are usually partial plots (the effect of these variables after the effects of all other relevant variables have been controlled experimentally or statistically).

> **If the axes on the graph represent anything other than the dimensions in our conclusion, we do not have convincing evidence for our conclusion.**

If we have carried out statistical manipulations, it may be necessary to report the probability values associated with the null hypotheses that we obtained from statistical tests. We have seen that statistical tests can often be replaced by simple graphs, and many authors state that statistical tests should never be used (see

Figure 13.1

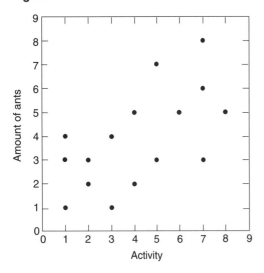

Harlick et al. 1997). However, we have also seen that data manipulations may make weak patterns appear stronger than they were in the raw data, and some techniques, such as discriminant function analysis and canonical correspondence analysis, produce graphs that may mislead us about the factors affecting our study organisms. Such graphs should never be presented without probabilistic justification.

Figure 13.1 is convincing; we can see that there is a strong relationship between foraging activity and the quantity of ants in the diet. However, in many studies, we find that the graph does not support the conclusion, and we have to modify the conclusion before continuing. Once we have the correct graph, we can proceed to writing the methods section. The methods section should present all of the information necessary to show how we obtained the data for the graph, and nothing else. It is usually not necessary to know that measurements were made in a room called a laboratory, or to know that we weighed the organism if mass does not appear in the analyses. Keep words to a minimum so that the reader's attention will stay focused on the important aspects, and this will maximize communication. Sometimes we have to modify the conclusion at this point, and start again, because we recognize some fatal flaw in the data collection protocol. Good researchers usually don't worry if they make a mistake; it shows that they have learned something.

In the methods section, we also have to explain why we believe that each point on the graph represents independent information in relation to the question (in other words, how we avoided pseudoreplication). If we have too many points for the number of independent observations, the graph will be misleading. We may have to create the graph again and re-evaluate our conclusions if we detect that we have plotted data that are not independent.

Having defined our conclusion, confident that the results really do lead to that conclusion, we are ready to write the introduction. This should contain only the minimum amount of information necessary to present the question for which our conclusion is the answer. The question may have been raised because of findings in the literature, information from experienced researchers, or preliminary observations. We need nothing else. Reviews of the literature about the taxonomy of the species, or statements about the necessity of conserving tropical forests, or other "scientific" discourses are only of relevance if they introduce the labels on the axes of our graphs.

Having defined our question(s) and answer(s), we can proceed to writing the discussion section. This should only present information (usually from the litera-ture) that supports, extends, modifies, or contradicts the conclusion(s) based on the data we presented. It is not a forum for presentation of conclusions that are not based on the data from your study. When you read other researchers' papers you do not want to wade through pages of speculation to try work out the relevance of the study.

The last thing to worry about is the title. The best titles are usually questions or answers (conclusions). Therefore, we could use the question, "Does the amount of

> **Therefore, do unto others as you would have them do unto you.**

ants in frog diets vary with foraging intensity?" or the answer, "The amount of ants in frog diets varies with foraging intensity." There are many different ways of expressing these ideas, but the critical point is that the dimensions in the conclu-sion (and in the question and graph) must be explicit in the title. Otherwise, potential readers will not know what to expect, and may not bother to read the paper.

If you are having trouble expressing your ideas, check that the sections of your paper are linked (Figure 13.2). This simple scheme is amazingly effective at iden-tifying communication problems. The authors of this book have a combined total of well over 100 scientific publications, but still have to refer to a conceptual flow chart, (such as that in Figure 13.2), when writing new papers. If you have too many "conclusions" it is because you have discovered nothing very exciting, or because you are confusing intermediate methodological results with the results that really affect your biological conclusions. Even very complex papers rarely have more than two or three major conclusions.

Annoying Yet Important Details

There are many other complications, especially when writ-ing "why" papers. We use the frog example to introduce a few of the most important ones faced by budding authors, but similar problems arise in all scientific fields. A com-mon mistake is to assume that our measurements corre-spond to conceptual quantities recognized by other researchers. All units of measure are indices of some the-oretical, physical or conceptual quantity. For example, to

Figure 13.2

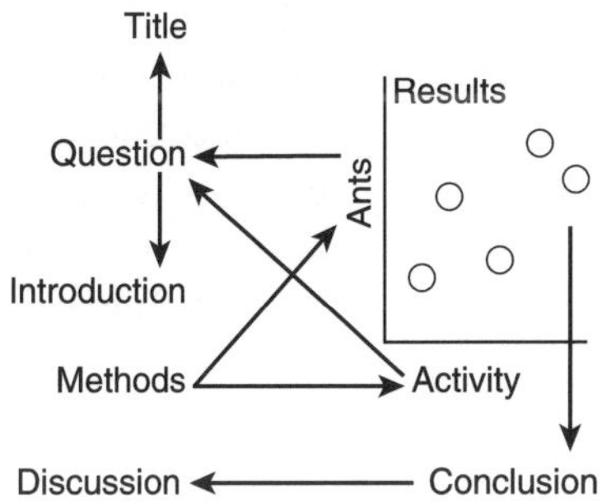

measure our frogs we used a ruler or calipers marked with standard distances. These standard distances bear an approximate relationship to a platinum-iridium bar preserved at the International Bureau of Weights and Measures located outside of Paris, which is kept at a steady temperature and pressure to avoid dilatation. We are interested in the size of frogs, and most researchers use body length as an index of size, but the dictionary definition of "size" is volume. Under the dictionary definition, mass would probably be a better index of size than length. A concept as simple as "size" can mean different things to different people.

Our graph has "amount of ants" on the y-axis, but we did not define "amount." Some researchers use number of prey items to represent "amount," some use prey volume, some use calorific content of prey, and several dozen other indices can be found in the literature. None of these is necessarily superior to the others; it all depends on the question. Problems arise when the researcher uses an index because it is frequently used by other researchers (a cultural norm), and not because it is appropriate to the question. For instance, many researchers use indices of volume of insect prey that are based on two linear measurements. The resulting estimates have little relationship with volume measured by fluid displacement (Magnusson et al. 2003). These researchers are using indices of volume that have no physical counterpart, so the potential for breakdown in communication is great.

"Intensity of foraging" is even more complicated. Researchers have used frequency of movement, distance moved per unit time, area covered per unit time, proportion of time in movement, multivariate combinations of these indices, and several others. Each of these indices tells us different things about the activity of frogs.

Using a standard index because it allows comparisons among studies only makes sense if all of the studies are investigating exactly the same question. Rather than

The correct choice of index can only be made after you have decided on the question.

undertaking a "me-too" study, it might be more interesting to ask a question that other researchers have not yet answered. Unfortunately, choosing an inappropriate index (measurement, variable) at the start of the study may limit us to answering questions that have already been answered, and that are no longer very interesting. Cunning researchers use a scheme like that in Figure 13.2, or something in addition to a hypothetical graph, to start "writing up" at the beginning of the study, before collecting any data.

"Why" Questions

We have determined that there is a relationship between foraging activity and the number of ants in the diet. That was easy, but the process gets complicated if we ask, "Why is there a relationship between foraging activity and the amount of ants in the diet?" Frogs that are more active tend to be bufonids (T for "toads" in Figure 13.3), and frogs that are less active tend to be from other families (F for "frogs" in Figure 13.3). Maybe the ancestors of toads just happened to be active and eat ants. If we are not interested in the effects of phylogenetic inertia, we could use phylogenetically independent contrasts (Garland et al. 1992) to remove the effects of genetic relatedness, or perhaps we could investigate whether diet and foraging are related within species, using individuals as sampling units. Depending on our question, phylogenetic effects may be the focus of our study, or they may just be nuisance variables that need to be controlled.

Numerous ecological hypotheses have been raised to explain the relationship between the amount of ants in the diet and the foraging behavior of frogs. Active frogs may encounter more ants because they tend to move around more. Frogs that eat ants may sequester poisons from their prey, making them unpalatable to their own enemies and therefore immune from attack as they move around. Ants may represent concentrated resources that can only be exploited by wide-foraging predators. Perhaps frogs can only be continuously active if they exploit a food source that has little tendency to fluctuate spatially or temporally. Some of these hypotheses indicate that differences in diet are passive reflections of foraging behavior, and others indicate that foraging behavior evolved to maximize encounters with ants. The situation is even more complicated, because what determines variation within species in the amount of ants in the diet may not be what determines differences between species in the amount of ants in the diet.

Figure 13.3

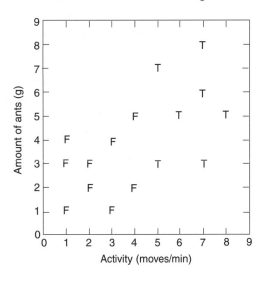

We do not have the answer to this "why" question. Many researchers are developing sophisticated experiments and sampling regimes to try to get closer to the answer. Maybe somebody will answer the question, or some aspects of the question, and maybe not. What we can be sure of is that an unequivocal answer to the question will not come from some standard statistical test taken from a textbook. We can also be sure that our confidence in the conclusion has little to do with the probability of encountering a regression line with a slope as extreme, or more extreme, than expected if the relationship between the amount of ants in the diet and activity of foraging were random.

Science advances slowly with the accumulation of answers to "how" and "what" questions, and leaps forward with answers to "why" questions. Great scientists and philosophers, such as Fisher and Popper, were interested in "why" questions. It is a shame that their names are generally associated with simple techniques that are most appropriate for answering "how" and "what" questions. Discovering how to answer a "why" question is an act of genius. You do that part, and our little recipe for writing will help you communicate your conclusion to other people.

A Final Comment

This book ends here. We hope that we have contributed to your capacity to interpret scientific literature, and to your ability to communicate your ideas clearly to fellow scientists. The ability to design good experiments is an art that cannot be taught by a book. However, we hope that we have pointed out a few of the most common problems that plague experimental designs, especially those that arise from our cultural baggage, and that easily go unnoticed because familiarity has accustomed us to them. The scientific academy has devoted years to convincing you that the most important thing is to *appear* to be a scientist, by dressing, talking, and writing in a complicated fashion that is believed to be the badge of a scientist. However, if you want to communicate the results of your research, you will have to do more than merely communicate cultural identity. If, after reading this book, you are tempted to try to present your results on simple graphs and use statistics to simplify rather than complicate answers, then our efforts will have been worthwhile.

INDEX

REFERENCES

Abuabara, M. A. P. and M. Petrere. 1997. Estimativas da Abundância de Populações Animais. EDUEM, Maringá.

Albert, J. 1997. Teaching Bayes' rule: A data oriented approach. American Statistician 51:247–253.

Allen, T. F. H. 1998. The landscape "level" is dead: Persuading the family to take it off the respirator. Pp. 35–54 In D. L. Peterson and V. T. Parker, eds. Ecological Scale. Colombia University Press, New York.

Allen, T. F. H and T. B. Starr. 1982. Hierarchy: Perspectives for Ecological Complexity. University of Chicago Press, Chicago.

Anderson, D. R., K. P. Burnham, G. C. White, and D. L. Otis. 1983. Density estimation of small-mammal populations using a trapping web and distance sampling methods. Ecology 64:674–680.

Anderson, D. R., K. P. Burnham, and W. L. Thompson. 2000. Null hypothesis testing: Problems, prevalence, and an alternative. Journal of Wildlife Management 64:912–923.

Anderson, D. R., K. P. Burnham, W. R. Gould, and S. Cherry. 2001. Concerns about finding effects that are actually spurious. Wildlife Society Bulletin 29(1):311–316.

Anderson, M. J. 2001. A new method for non-parametric multivariate analysis of variance. Austral Ecology 26:32–46.

Anderson. M. J. and T. J. Willis. 2003. Canonical analysis of principal coordinates: A useful method of constrained ordination for ecology. Ecology 84(2):511–525.

Anderson, M. and P. Legendre. 1999. An empirical comparison of permutation methods for tests of partial regression coefficients in a linear model. Journal of Statistical and Computer Simulation 62:271–303.

Anscombe, F. J. 1973. Graphs in statistical analysis. American Statistician 27:17–21.

Austin, M. P. 2002. Spatial prediction of species distribution: An interface between ecological theory and statistical modelling. Ecological Modelling 157:101–118.

Azevedo-Ramos, C., W. E. Magnusson, and P. Bayliss. 1999. Predation as a key factor structuring tadpole assemblages in a savanna area in central Amazonia. Copeia 1999:22–33.

Bard, Y. 1974. Nonlinear Parameter Estimation. Academic Press, New York.

Basford, K. E. and J. W. Tukey. 1999. Graphical Analysis of Multi-Response Data Illustrated with a Plant Breeding Trial: Interdisciplinary Statistics. Chapman and Hall, Boca Raton.

Belbin, L. 1992. PATN Pattern Analysis Package—Technical Reference. CSIRO, Canberra.

Benedetti-Cecchi, L. 2003. The importance of the variance around the mean effect size on ecological processes. Ecology 84:2335–2346.

Benjamini, Y. and Y. Hochberg. 1995. Controlling the false discovery rate: A practical and powerful approach to multiple testing. Journal of the Royal Statistical Society 57 (Series B): 289–300.

Bennington, C. C. and W. V. Thayne. 1994. Use and misuse of mixed model analysis of variance in ecological studies. Ecology 75:717–722.

Berk, K. N. 1978. Comparing subset selection procedures. Technometrics 20:1–6.

Beyer, W. H. 1968. Handbook of Probability and Statistics. CRC Press, Boca Raton, Florida, USA.

Borg, I. and P. Groenen. 1997. Modern Multidimensional Scaling: Theory and Applications. Springer, New York, USA 135.

Bradshaw, G. A. 1998. Defining ecologically relevant change in the process of scaling up: Implications for monitoring at the landscape level. Pp. 227–249 In D. L. Peterson and V. T. Parker, eds. Ecological Scale. Colombia University Press, New York.

Braun-Blanquet, J. 1932. Plant Sociology: The Study of Plant Communities. Hafner, London.

Brown, I. F. 1997. Let the people judge: Community examining boards help students learn to communicate. Bulletin of the Ecological Society of America 78:210–211.

Burnham, K. P. and D. R. Anderson. 1998. Model selection and inference: A practical information-theoretic approach. Springer-Verlag, New York.

Cade, B. S., J. W. Terrell, and R. L. Schroeder. 1999. Estimating regression effects of limiting factors with regression quantiles. Ecology 80:311–323.

Callaghan, A. and G. J. Holloway. 1999. The relationship between environmental stress and variance. Ecological Applications 9:456–462.

Carlson, J. M. and J. Doyle. 1999. Highly optimized tolerance: A mechanism for power laws in designed systems. Physical Review E 60:1412–1427.

Carpenter, S. R. 1999. Microcosm experiments have limited relevance for community and ecosystem ecology: A reply. Ecology 80:1085–1088.

Caughley, G. and A. R. E. Sinclair. 1994. Wildlife Ecology and Management. Blackwell Scientific Publications, Oxford.

Cherry, S. 1999. Statistical tests in publications of The Wildlife Society. Wildlife Society Bulletin 26: 947–953.

Connolly, J., P. Wayne, and F. A. Bazzaz. 2001. Interspecific competition in plants: How well do current methods answer fundamental questions. American Naturalist 157:107–125.

Dale, M. B. 1988. Knowing when to stop: Cluster concept—concept cluster. Coenoses 3:11–32.

Day, R. W. and G. P. Quinn. 1989. Comparisons of treatments after an analysis of variance in ecology. Ecological Monographs 59:433–463.

De'ath, G. 1999. Principal curves: A new technique for indirect and direct gradient analysis. Ecology 80:2237–2253.

Deming, W. E. 1975. On probability as a basis for action. American Statistician 29:146–152.

Dytham, C. 1999. Choosing and Using Statisitics: A Biologist's Guide. Blackwell Science, Oxford.

Ehrenberg, A. S. C. 1981. The problem of numeracy. American Statistician 35:67–71.

Ellison, A. M. 1993. Exploratory data analysis and graphic display. Pp. 14–45 In S. M. Scheiner and J. Gurevitch, eds. Design and Analysis of Ecological Experiments. Chapman and Hall, New York.

Faith, D. P., P. R. Minchin, and L. Belbin 1987. Compositional dissimilarity as a robust measure of ecological distance: A theoretical model and computer simulations. Vegetatio 69:57–68.

Feinsinger, P. 2002. Designing Field Studies for Biodiversity Conservation. Island Press, Washington, USA.

Fortin, M. J. and J. Gurevitch 1993. Mantel tests: Spatial structure in field experiments. Pp. 342–352 *In* S. M. Scheiner and J. Gurevitch, eds. *Design and Analysis of Ecological Experiments.* Chapman and Hall, New York.

Fowler, N. 1990. The 10 most common statistical errors. Bulletin of the Ecological Society of America 71:161–164.

Freedman, D. A. 1983. A note on screening regression equations. American Statistician 37:152–155.

Friendly, M. 1995. Conceptual and visual models for categorical data. American Statistician 49:153–160.

Gaines, S. D. and W. R. Rice. 1990. Analysis of biological data when there are ordered expectations. American Naturalist 135:310–317.

Garland, T., P. H. Harvey, and A. R. Ives. 1992. Procedures for the analysis of comparative data using phylogenetically independent contrasts. Systematic Biology 41:18–32.

Gauch, H. G. 1982a. *Multivariate Analysis in Community Ecology.* Cambridge University Press, Cambridge.

Gauch, H. G. 1982b. Noise reduction by eigenvector ordinations. Ecology 63:1643–1649.

Goleman, D. 1995. *Emotional Intelligence.* Bloomsbury Publishing, London.

Green, R. H. 1989. Power analysis and statistical strategies for environmental monitoring. Environmental Research 50:195–205.

Guisan, A., T. C. Edwards, and T. Hastie. 2002. Generalized linear and generalized additive models in studies of species distributions: Setting the scene. Ecological Modelling 157:89–100.

Guttman, L. 1985. The illogic of statistical inference for cumulative science. Applied Stochastic Models and Data Analysis 1:3–10.

Hairston, N. G. 1989. Hard choices in ecological experimentation. Herpetologica 45:119–122.

Hale, S. S. 1999. How to manage data badly (part 1). Bulletin of the Ecological Society of America 80:265–268.

Hall, E. T. 1959. *The Silent Language.* Doubleday and Company, New York.

Hallgren, E., M. W. Palmer, and P. Milberg. 1999. Data diving with cross-validation: An investigation of broad-scale gradients in Swedish weed communities. Journal of Ecology 87:1037–1051.

Harris, R. J. 1975. *A Primer for Multivariate Statistics.* Academic Press, New York.

Higashi, M. and T. P. Burns. 1991. *Theoretical Studies of Ecosystems: The Network Perspective.* Cambridge University Press, Cambridge.

Hilborn, R. and M. Mangel. 1997. *The Ecological Detective.* Princeton University Press, Princeton.

Hobbs, R. J. 1998. Managing ecological systems and processes. Pp. 459–484 *In* D. L. Peterson and V. T. Parker, eds. *Ecological Scale.* Colombia University Press, New York.

Huberty, C. J. 1987. On statistical testing. Educational Researcher 16:4–9.

Hurlbert, S. H. 1984. Pseudoreplication and the design of ecological field experiments. Ecological Monographs 54:187–211.

Iglewicz, B. 1983. Robust scale estimators and confidence intervals for location. Pp. 404–431 *In* D. C. Hoaglin, F. Mosteller, and J. W. Tukey, eds. *Understanding Robust and Exploratory Data Analysis.* John Wiley and Sons, New York.

Jackson, D. A. 1993. Stopping rules in principal components analysis: A comparison of heuristical and statistical approaches. Ecology 74:2204–2214.

Jackson, D. A. 1997. Compositional data in community ecology: The paradigm or peril of proportions. Ecology 78(3):929–940.

James, F. C. and C. E. McCulloch. 1990. Multivariate analysis in ecology and systematics: Panacea or Pandora's box? Annual Review of Ecology and Systematics 21:129–166.

Johnson, C. R. and C. C. Field. 1993. Using fixed-effects model multivariate analysis of variance in marine biology and ecology. Oceanography and Marine Biology Annual Review 31:177–221.

Johnson, D. H. 1999. The insignificance of statistical significance testing. Journal of Wildlife Management 63:763–772.

Kenckel, N. C. and L. Orloci. 1986. Applying metric and non-metric multidimensional scaling to ecological studies: Some new results. Ecology 67:919–928.

Koele, P. 1982. Calculating power in analysis of variance. Psychological Bulletin 92:513–516.

Krebs, C. J. 1989. *Ecological Methodology.* Harper and Row, New York.

Kruskal, W. 1988. Miracles and statistics: The casual assumption of independence. Journal of the American Statistical Association 83:929–940.

Kuhn, T. S. 1970. *The Structure of Scientific Revolutions*, 2nd Edition. University of Chicago Press, Chicago.

Lawton, J. 1999. Size matters. Oikos 85:19–21.

Legendre, P. 1993. Spatial autocorrelation: Trouble or a new paradigm? Ecology 74:1659–1673.

Legendre, P. and L. Legendre. 1998. *Numerical Ecology: Second English Edition.* Elsevier, Amsterdam.

Legendre, P. and M. J. Anderson. 1999. Distance-based redundancy analysis: Testing multispecies responses in multifactorial ecological experiments. Ecological Monographs 69:1–28.

Legendre, P. and E. D. Gallagher. 2001. Ecologically meaningful transformations for ordination of species data. Oecologia 129:271–280.

Lennon, J. L. 2000. Red-shifts and red herrings in geographical ecology. Ecography 23:101–113.

Link, W. A. 1999. Modeling patterns in collections of parameters. Journal of Wildlife Management 63:1017–1027.

Luo, J. and B. J. Fox. 1996. A review of the Mantel test in dietary studies: Effect of sample size and inequality of sample sizes. Wildlife Research 23:267–288.

McCune, B. 1997. Influence of noisy environmental data on canonical correspondence analysis. Ecology 78:2617–2623.

McCune, B. and J. B. Grace. 2002. *Analysis of Ecological Communities.* MjM Software Design, Gleneden Beach, OR.

Mac Nally, R. C. 1994. On characterizing foraging versatility, illustrated by using birds. Oikos 69:95–106.

Mac Nally, R. C. 2002. Multiple regression and inference in ecology and conservation biology: Further comments on identifying important predictor variables. Biodiversity and Conservation 11:1397–1401.

Magee, B. 1976. *Popper.* Fontana, London.

Magnusson, W. E. 1997. Teaching experimental design, or how to do statistics without a bikini. Bulletin of the Ecological Society of America 78:205–209.

Magnusson, W. E. 1999. Spatial independence: The importance of the question. Wildlife Society Bulletin 27:1112–1113.

Magnusson, W. E. 2000a. Error bars: Are they the King's clothes? Bulletin of the Ecological Society of America. 81:147–150.

Magnusson, W. E. 2000b. Statistical iatrogenesis: Cure it or prevent it? Bulletin of the Ecological Society of America 81:198–201.

Magnusson, W. E. 2001. Standard errors of survey estimates: What do they mean? Neotropical Primates 9:53–54.

Magnusson, W. E. 2002. Diversity indices: Multivariate candies from Pandora's box. Bulletin of the Ecological Society of America 83:86–87.

Magnusson, W. E. 2002a. Categorical ANOVA: Strong inference for weak data. Bulletin of the Ecological Society of America 83:81–86.

Makarenkov V. and P. Legendre. 2002. Nonlinear redundancy analysis and canonical correspondence analysis based on polynomial regression. Ecology 83:1146–1161.

Manel, S., J. M. Dias, S. T. Buxton, and S. J. Ormerod. 1999. Alternative methods for predicting species distribution: An illustration with Himalayan river birds. Journal of Applied Ecology 36:734–747.

Manly, B. F. J. 1997. *Randomization, Bootstrap and Monte Carlo Methods in Biology*. Chapman and Hall, London.

Mantel, N. A. and R. S. Valand. 1970. A technique for nonparametric multivariate analysis. Biometrics 26:547–558.

McArdle, B. H. and M. J. Anderson. 2001. Fitting multivariate models to community data: A comment on distance-based redundancy analysis. Ecology 82:290–297.

Meeks, S. L. and R. B. D'Agostino. 1983. A note on the use of confidence limits following rejection of a null hypothesis. American Statistician 37:134–136.

Meot, A., P. Legendre, and D. Borcard. 1998. Partialling out the spatial component of ecological variation: Questions and propositions in the linear modelling framework. Environmental and Ecological Statistics 5:1–27.

Milligan, G. W. and M. C. Cooper. 1985. An examination of procedures for determining the number of clusters in a data set. Psychometrika 50:159–179.

Minchin, P. R. 1987. Simulation of multidimensional community patterns: Toward a comprehensive model. Vegetatio 71:145–156.

Moore, D. S. 1997. Bayes' for beginners? Some reasons to hesitate. American Statistician 51: 254–261.

Mosteller, F. and J. W. Tukey. 1968. Data analysis, including statistics. Pp. 80–203 In G. Lindzey and E. Aronson, eds. *Handbook of Social Psychology*, 2nd Edition, Volume 2. Addison-Wesley, Reading, Massachusetts.

Newman, J. A., J. Bergelson, and A. Grafen. 1997. Blocking factors and hypothesis tests in ecology: Is your statistics text wrong? Ecology 78:1312–1320.

Neyman, J. 1937. Outline of a theory of statistical estimation based on the classical theory of probability. Philosophical Transactions of the Royal Society of London Series A 231:333–380.

Noy-Meir, I., D.Walker, and W. T. Williams. 1975. Data transformations in ecological ordination. II. On the meaning of data standardization. Journal of Ecology 63:779–800.

Økland, R. H. 1996. Are ordination and constrained ordination alternative or complementary strategies in general ecological studies? Journal of Vegetation Science 7:289–292.

Økland, R. H. 1999. On the variation explained by ordination and constrained ordination axes. Journal of Vegetation Science 10:131–136.

Oksanen, J. and P. R. Minchin. 1997. Instability of ordination results under changes in input data order: Explanations and remedies. Journal of Vegetation Science 8:447–454.

Oksanen, J. and P. R. Minchin. 2002. Continuum theory revisited: What are species responses along ecological gradients? Journal of Vegetation Science 8:447–454.

Olson, C. L. 1976. On choosing a test statistic in multivariate analysis of variance. Psychological Bulletin 83:579–586.

O'Neill, R. V. and A. W. King. 1998. Homage to St Michael; or why are there so many books on scale? Pp. 3–15 In D. L. Peterson and V. T. Parker, eds. *Ecological Scale*. Colombia University Press, New York.

Ormerod, S. J., M. W. Pienkowsky, and A. R. Watkinson. 1999. Communicating the value of ecology. Journal of Applied Ecology 36:847–855.

Osenberg, C. W., O. Sarnelle, S. D. Cooper, and R. D. Holt. 1999. Resolving ecological questions through meta-analysis: Goals, metrics, and models. Ecology 80(4):1105–1117.

Palmer, A. R. 1999. Detecting publication bias in meta-analyses: A case study of fluctuating asymmetry and sexual selection. 154:220–233.

Parmenter, R. R., T. L. Yates, D. R. Anderson, K. P. Burnham, J. L. Dunnum, A. B, Franklin, M. T. Friggens, B. C. Lubow, M. Miller, G. S. Olson, C. A. Parmenter, J. Pollard, E. Rexstad, T. M. Shenk, T. R. Stanley, and G. C. White. 2003. Small-mammal density estimation: a field comparison of grid-based vs web-based density estimates. Ecological Monographs 73:1–26.

Pascual, M. and S. A. Levin. 1999. From individuals to population densities: Searching for the intermediate scale of nontrivial determinism. Ecology 80:2225–2236.

Pearson, K. 1901. On lines and planes of closest fit to systems of points in space. Philosophical Magazine 6:559–572.

Peladeau, N. 1966. *Simstat for Windows*. Provalis Research. Montreal, QC., Canada.

Pélissier, R., P. Couteron, S. Dray, and P. Sabatier. 2003. Consistency between ordination techniques and diversity measurements: Two strategies for species occurrence data. Ecology 84:242–251.

Peres-Neto, P. R., and D. A. Jackson. 2001. How well do multivariate data sets match? The advantages of a Procrustean superimposition approach over the Mantel test. Oecologia 129:169–178.

Peterson, D. L. and V. T. Parker, eds. 1998. *Ecological Scale*. Colombia University Press, New York.

Petersen, J. E., J. C. Cornwell, and W. M. Kemp. 1999. Implicit scaling in the design of experimental aquatic ecosystems. Oikos 85:3–18.

Petraitis, P. S., A. E. Dunham, and P. H. Niewarowski. 1996. Inferring multiple causality: The limitations of path analysis. Functional Ecology 10:421–431.

Picard, R. R. and R. D. Cook. 1984. Cross-validation of regression models. Journal of the American Statistical Association 79:575–583.

Pickett, S. T. A., J. Kolasa, and C. G. Jones. 1994. *Ecological Understanding*. Academic Press. San Diego.

Pielou, E. C. 1984. *The Interpretation of Ecological Data*. Wiley, New York.

Pillar, V. D. 1999. How sharp are classifications? Ecology 80(8):2508–2516.

Platt, J. R. 1964. Strong inference. Science 146:347–353.

Polis, G. A. 1999. Why are parts of the world green? Multiple factors control productivity and distribution of biomass. Oikos 86:3–15.

Popper, K. R. 1976. *Unended Quest: An Intellectual Autobiography*. Fontana, London.

Powell, T. M. and J. H. Steele. 1995. *Ecological Time Series*. Chapman and Hall, New York.

Rice, W. R. 1989. Analyzing tables of statistical tests. Evolution 43:223–225.

Ricker, W. E. 1973. Linear regressions in fishery research. Journal of the Fish Research Board of Canada. 30:409–434.

Rosenthal, R. and D. B. Rubin. 1982. A simple general purpose display of magnitude of experimental effect. Journal of Educational Psychology 74:166–169.

Rosenthal, R. and D. B. Rubin. 1994. The counternull value of an effect size: A new statistic. Psychological Science 5:329–334.

Salsburg, D. 2001. *The Lady Tasting Tea: How Statistics Revolutionized Science in the Twentieth Century*. W. H. Freeman, New York.

Salsburg, D. S. 1985. The religion of statistics as practiced in medical journals. American Statistician 39:220–223.

Sawada, M. 1999. Rookcase: An excel 97/2000 visual basic (VB) add-in for exploring global and local spatial autocorrelation. Bulletin of the Ecological Society of America 80:231–234.

Shipley, B. 1999. Testing causal explanations in organismal biology: Causation, correlation and structural equation modelling. Oikos 86:374–382.

Short, J., G. Caughley, D. Grice, and B. Brown. 1983. The distribution and abundance of kangaroos in relation to environment in Western Australia. Australian Wildlife Research 10:435–451.

Smouse, P. E., J. C. Long, and R. R. Sokal. 1986. Multiple regression and correlation extensions of the Mantel test of matrix correspondence. Systematic Zoology 35:627–632.

Sokal, R. R. and F. J. Rohlf. 1995. *Biometry*, 3rd Edition. W. H. Freeman and Company, New York.

Spitz, F. and S. Leks. 1999. Environmental impact prediction using neural network modelling. An example in wildlife damage. Journal of Applied Ecology 36:317–326.

Starfield, A. M. and A. L. Bleloch. 1991. *Building Models for Conservation and Wildlife Management*. Bellwether Press, Edina, Minnesota.

Stern, M. J. 1998. Field comparisons of two rapid vegetation assessment techniques with permanent plot inventory data in Amazonian Peru. Pp. 269–283 *In* F. Dallmeier and J. A. Comiskey, eds. *Forest Biodiversity Research, Monitoring and Modeling*. UNESCO and Parthenon Publishing, Paris.

Stigler, S. M. 1986. *The History of Statistics: The Measurement of Uncertainty before 1900*. Belknap Press, Cambridge Massachusetts.

Student (W.S. Gosset).1908. The probable error of the mean. Biometrika 6:1–25.

ter Braak, C. J. F. 1986. Canonical correspondence analysis: A new eigenvector technique for multivariate direct gradient analysis. Ecology 86:1167–1179.

Thompson, G. G. and P. C. Withers. 2003. Effect of species richness and relative abundance on the shape of species accumulation curve. Austral Ecology 28:355–360.

Thornhill, R., A. P. Moller, and S. W. Gangestad. 1999. The biological significance of fluctuating asymmetry and sexual selection: A reply to Palmer. American Naturalist 154:234–241.

Tukey, J. W. 1960. Conclusions vs. decisions. Technometrics 2:423–433.

Tukey, J. W. 1972. Some graphic and semigraphic displays. Pp. 293–316 *In* T. A. Bancroft, ed. *Statistical Papers in Honour of George W. Snedecor*. Iowa State Press, Ames, Iowa.

Tukey, J. W. 1980. We need both exploratory and confirmatory. American Statistician 34:23–25.

Tukey, J. W. 1991. The philosophy of multiple comparisons. Statistical Science 6:100–116.

von Ende, C. N. 1993. Repeated measures analysis: Growth and other time-dependent measures. Pp. 113–137 *In* S. M. Scheiner and J. Gurevitch, eds. *Design and Analysis of Ecological Experiments*. Chapman and Hall, New York.

Wallace, C. S. and D. L. Dowe. 2000. MML clustering of multistate, Poisson, von Mises circular and Gaussian distributions. Statistics and Computing 10:73–83.

Wardle, G. M. 1998. A graph theory approach to demographic loop analysis. Ecology 79:2539–2549.

Wartenberg, D., S. Ferson, and F. J. Rohlf. 1987. Putting things in order: A critique of detrended correspondence analysis. American Naturalist 129:434–448.

Wilkinson, L. 1999. Statistical methods in psychology journals: Guidelines and explanations. American Psychologist 54:594–604.

Williams, B. K. 1983. Some observations on the use of discriminant analysis in ecology. Ecology 64:1283–1291.

Williams, B. K. and K. Titus 1988. Assessment of sampling stability in ecological applications of discriminant analysis. Ecology 69:1275–1291.

Winer, B. J., D. R. Brown, and K. M. Michaels. 1991. *Statistical Principles in Experimental Design*. McGraw-Hill, New York.

Wood, S. N. 1997. Inverse problems and structured-population dynamics. Pp. 555–586 *In* S. Tuljapurkar and H. Caswell, eds. *Structured-Population Models in Marine, Terrestrial, and Freshwater Systems*. Chapman and Hall, New York.

Yoccoz, N. G. 1991. Use, overuse, and misuse of significance tests in evolutionary biology and ecology. Bulletin of the Ecological Society of America 72:106–111.

Zar, J. H. 1996. *Biostatistical Analysis*, 4th Edition. Prentice-Hall, London.